THE
GRINDING
MACHINE

THE
GRINDING
MACHINE

Ian Bradley

MODEL & ALLIED PUBLICATIONS
LIMITED

Model and Allied Publications Ltd.
Book Division, Station Road,
Kings Langley, Herts., England.

First Published 1973

ISBN 0 85242 324 1

Printed in Great Britain by Offset Litho at
Gilmour & Dean Ltd., Hamilton, Scotland.

Bound in Great Britain at
The Pitman Press, Bath, Somerset.

CONTENTS

PREFACE

OF ALL THE MACHINES in the amateur or small workshop, perhaps the one that always seems to be taken for granted is the Grinding Machine. In its simplest form as used for tool grinding, it performs, when correctly used, one of the most important services in the shop. Yet little written instruction or advice about the machine seems to be available to those most in need of it. Nothing is said about its operation, its maintenance, or the correct treatment of the abrasive wheels mounted on its spindle; the user being left to discover these things for himself.

If we can accept the premise that sharp tools, in their many forms, are essential to satisfactory workshop practice, there is, perhaps, no need to make excuses for having written this book.

Hungerford 1972   I.B.

CHAPTER ONE

GRINDING MEDIA

FOR CENTURIES MAN has made use of natural stones and other mineral compounds for sharpening his tools. For the most part these materials involved the application of a reciprocating movement to the tool itself while the stone remains stationary. Some of the older materials are still of interest, not only for their continued use in hand honing but for the fact that they may be formed into wheels and used for the fine finishing of many items such as scribers, centre punches and turning tools all needing a high finish for special purposes.

The Arkansas Stone

One of the best known natural abrasives is the Arkansas Stone, so called from the area in which it is found, the State of Arkansas in America. It is a white stone of almost pure quartz without grain and of extreme hardness and undoubtedly the best abrasive to impart a fine and keen edge to all cutting tools. Needless to say it is expensive and so deserves to be treated with care and protected from any damage caused by mishandling. This applies to those stones in particular that are used on the bench and might be ruined by being dropped or having something fall on them.

The Washita Stone

Greatly inferior to and much cheaper than the former stone, Washita is rougher, is open grained and much softer and very liable to scoring if pointed or narrow edged tools are being sharpened.

To secure the best results both stones need to be lubricated with thin oil in order to prevent "loading" and to promote free cutting.

Both materials can be obtained as wheels, but it is those made from Arkansas stone that are the most satisfactory and to which we shall be referring later.

Over the centuries the quality of edged tools together with their means of production had steadily improved. Naturally, means were sought to speed up the process of sharpening, for neither the abrasives available, nor the hand methods employed to produce a keen edge, were capable of coping with the work speedily.

Mechanical methods were therefore tried, in particular rotating stones, turned at first by water power and later by steam, in an effort to reduce the drudgery and to speed up the sharpening process. Of the natural stones tried, and possibly because it was the only one that could be fashioned into the form of a wheel easily, sandstone came to be accepted as the most practical abrasive material to use. Grindstones cut from natural sandstone, some of them very large indeed, were much employed in the cutlery industry while they were also found, and may sometimes still be found, in some carpenters' shops.

Owing to its soft nature the stone must not be used dry; so either it has an arrangement allowing water to trickle on to its surface, or the stone is made to turn in a water trough as depicted in *Fig. 1.1.*

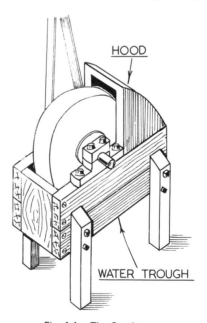

Fig. 1.1   The Sandstone.

The direction of rotation was varied. Some preferred the wheel to turn towards them, other liked it to turn in the opposite direction, as there was then no possibility of a "dig-in" taking place and ruining the surface of the stone.

The sandstone is probably the best medium for truing up the carpenter's plane iron. It cuts fast enough and cannot possibly burn the iron because of the cooling action of the water.

Advances in workshop technology over the years required improvements in tool grinding technique; so a search was made for a natural abrasive that could be bonded together to form a wheel that would cut far faster than the wet sandstone. Large deposits of emery and corundum were discovered. These materials were pulverised to produce a substance of fairly uniform grain size, and then bonded with either clay or pottery into wheels of varying diameters. For a while these satisfied industrial demand; but the variable quality and hardness of the natural material, coupled with the apparent difficulty of obtaining uniform grain size, led to further investigation. This culminated in the production of artificial abrasives that had all the attributes needed, moreover the material, carborundum, was of extreme hardness; only slightly less so than the diamond which is the hardest known substance.

Carborundum

The word "carborundum" is a trade name for one of the two basic materials manufactured by the Carborundum Company of Trafford Park, Manchester. This artificial abrasive is made by heating together a mixture of sand, coke, sawdust and salt in a resistance-type electric furnace, the process combining together the silicon of the sand with the carbon of the coke and sawdust to form silicon carbide. The resulting crystalline substance is crushed, washed with acids and alkalies to get rid of any impurities there may be, then graded to the correct size before being made into grinding wheels.

Aloxite

The other artificial abrasive made by the Carborundum Company is Aloxite. This is made by heating Bauxite in an arc-type electric furnace to form Aluminium Oxide, a hard crystalline substance that is then treated in the same way as Carborundum.

The characteristics of the two materials are as follows:— "Carborundum" is much harder than "Aloxite", it is also lighter in weight.

Aloxite is a very tough crystalline structure that will withstand heavy loading.

There are several bonds used when making grinding wheels. For the most part, however, wheels are bonded either by a vitrified process or directly by sodium silicate. In the vitrification process the abrasive is mixed with clays having the right characteristics, then, when the mixture is moulded in a hydraulic press and fired in kilns, a bond of high temperature glass or porcelain is formed.

Silicate wheels are, as has been said, bonded directly. They have a mild cutting action and should not be subjected to heavy loading. They are used principally in sharpening fine edged tools such as knives and the like.

We must now consider the system employed to classify abrasive wheels so that the user or purchaser can identify them correctly.

Identification consists for the most part in labelling the wheel with the size of the grit used in its make up, (this characteristic is also sometimes termed grain size), and its Grade.

Grit or Grain sizes

These are based on the meshes through which the abrasive will pass after crushing. For example a 46 grit will pass through a sieve having 46 meshes to the linear inch. The following table gives the Standard Grit Sizes used in connection with abrasive wheels:—

Very Coarse	*Coarse*	*Medium*	*Fine*	*Very Fine*
6	12	30	70	150
8	14	36	80	180
10	16	40 or 46	90	220
	20	50 or 54	100	240
	24	60	120	

Grade

This is a term not well understood. It is often confused with the hardness of the abrasive material composing the grinding wheel itself, whereas, in fact, it represents the tenacity with which the abrasive grains are retained in the wheel under load by the particular bonding medium employed. It is, therefore, a measure of the result of both grain and bond acting together. Wheel Grade is denoted by letters of the alphabet from D very hard to W very soft, according to the following table:—

Bond	Extra Hard	Hard	Medium	Soft		Very Soft
Vitrified	D	F G H	I J K L M	N O P	R S T	U V W
	E					
Silicate	D	F G H	I J K L M	N O P	R S T	U V W
	E					

It will be seen that the same letter coding is applied to either vitrified or silicate bonded wheels and their grading is therefore similar.

Grinding wheels have paper labels affixed to each side and on these are printed the letter and number references for the particular wheel to which the labels are attached. An example taken from the Carborundum Company might be labelled as follows:—

A 46—S—180

Where A is the abrasive in this case Aloxite AA
46 is the size of the abrasive grains
S is the Grade
180 is the particular bond used

When used for off-hand grinding, for the most part the finished wheel is furnished with a lead bushing upon which the wheel is mounted. The makers make use of this as a datum for truing the wheel before it is released for service, so ensuring that when the eventual purchaser mounts the wheel on the spindle of his grinding machine it will run approximately true.

The design of the spindle and the correct method of mounting the grinding wheel itself are matters of importance that will be dealt with in a later chapter.

CHAPTER TWO

HISTORICAL ASPECTS

IN THE PREVIOUS CHAPTER we have discussed various media that can be used for grinding purposes. In addition a machine commonly employed for tool sharpening was described. Historically this machine in its basic form has been known since about 850 A.D. when it was described and illustrated in the Utrecht Psalter. The stone used was natural sandstone, while the work for which the machine was employed was the sharpening of military weapons of war such as swords and spears. The stone was turned by hand, a second man being required for the job.

It was not till 1485 A.D. that an illustration of a treadle operated grindstone was described and depicted by one Israel von Meckenhem. By 1500 illustrations of treadle driven stones were becoming common.

About this time Leonardo da Vinci, that engineering genius, became interested in grinding techniques. As might be expected the designs that came from his drawing board were far superior to anything that had been put forward previously. Indeed, it has often been said that the technology of his times was unlikely to have been sufficiently far advanced to support da Vinci's somewhat revolutionary ideas. Be that as it may, it is certain that, on the design side at least, he provided possible solutions to grinding problems as he had done for many other mechanical devices.

Leonardo da Vinci's designs all seem to have envisaged power drive, either by water wheels or by the direct employment of horses. He does not however, seem to have paid much attention to the humble grindstone, which seems somewhat surprising. By 1568 powered grindstones were becoming common. The requirements of the military, with their complex pieces of armour that required elaborate polishing procedures and the many weapons that needed to be sharpened, soon led to installations in which some very large stones were power driven. Polishing and sharpening shops for various tools and equipment became universal during the next one hundred years, all of them being power driven by one means or another.

While the use of natural stone was almost a universal practice, the advantages of an artificial abrasive had been apparent to both India and China for centuries. Natural emery formed the basis of stones made in those centuries, the material being bonded together with a fusible element called "lac". Unfortunately, the bond was insufficiently strong to permit wheels being run at speeds that would allow the emery grains to cut efficiently. Modern wheels, however, can be run at high speeds without risk of disintegration, so surface speeds of from 5000 to 6000 feet per minute, a rate at which efficient cutting takes place, can be employed without danger.

Machines to use artificial abrasive wheels are the natural product of the Industrial Revolution both in this country and elsewhere. An example taken from the 9th edition of the Encyclopaedia Brittanica of 1878 and reproduced here as *Fig. 2.1*, shows that it was

FIG. 15.—Emery Shaping Machine.

Fig. 2.1   Grinder of 1878.

a simply conceived construction consisting of a cast iron base supporting a pair of plummer blocks in which ran a spindle carrying two grinding wheels. In addition to a pair of tool rests, used when sharpening tools on the rim of the wheels, each wheel was furnished with a table set above it to permit some elementary surface grinding to be performed. The wheel itself was allowed to project through the table, so by adjusting the table height it was possible to regulate the depth of cut if only somewhat roughly. The rudiments of the arrangement are illustrated in *Fig. 2.2*.

One remembers that the late Edgar Westbury once put forward a similar device as a possible piece of equipment for use in the amateur workshop.

Mounting the Grinding Wheel

In 1863 Phillipp introduced a wheel mounting that is essentially the same as that in use today. Phillipp's method, depicted in *Fig. 2.3*, employed relieved flanges that bore directly on the sides of the wheel itself whereas modern mountings employ paper washers between the flanges and the wheel.

The fixed flange was secured by a pin passing through the spindle of the machine, while the grinding wheel itself, set on a centralising bush, was held in place by the outer flange. The force necessary to provide the clamping action needed to hold the wheel appears to have been imparted by a pair of folding wedges, devices that have an inherent safety factor greater than could be expected from a single cottar pin.

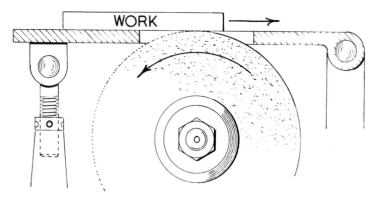

Fig. 2.2   Elementary Surface Grinder.

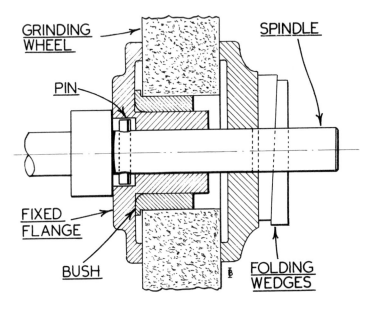

Fig. 2.3   Wheel Mounting 1863.

The modern method of mounting the grinding wheel employs a pair of relieved flanges, one fixed and one sliding, with the wheel centralised by a lead bush set in place during its manufacture. Paper washers affixed to the wheel are interposed to prevent the flanges having direct contact with the abrasive surface and nuts turning on the spindle provide the clamping force needed. Where there are two wheels mounted on a grinding machine the wheel on the right has a nut with a right-hand thread, the left-hand wheel having a nut with a left-hand thread. The normal arrangement as applied to off-hand grinding machines is depicted in *Fig. 2.4.*

Grinding as a means of stock removal was developed in America in order to hasten the quality production of parts needed in the manufacture of sewing machines, bicycles and, later, automobiles. The latter probably did more to promote this development than anything else. Both cylindrical and surface grinding were involved, for it was soon realised that the technique could do much to solve the problem of parts interchangeability and the search for operating silence.

The development work occupied the period from 1820 to 1870 being confined, for the most part, to two principal firms in America who specialised in the making the necessary equipment and the grinding wheels used in the process.

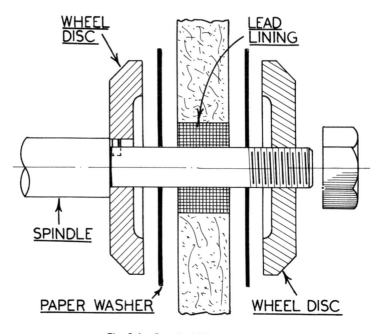

Fig. 2.4   Standard Wheel Mounting.

CHAPTER THREE

THE SIMPLE
TOOL GRINDER

IN CONNECTION WITH GRINDING EQUIPMENT for the amateur work-shop undoubtedly it is the tool grinding machine that is of the utmost importance. During the latter part of the last century, and the early part of this, power in the shop was supplied sometimes by a steam engine, sometimes by a gas or oil engine, and occasionally by a single electric motor. All of these prime movers involved the use of lineshafting for transmitting power to the machine tools, and this of course included the tool grinder. Some machines needed a simple countershaft, others, like the grinder illustrated in *Fig. 3.1,*

Fig. 3.1   Grinder with built-in striking gear.

11

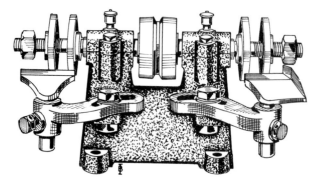

Fig. 3.2   Small bench grinding head.

Fig. 3.3   Small bench grinding head.

were provided with striking gear so could be driven directly from the lineshafting.

The advent of the small electric motor simplified many of the power problems in the workshop, the lineshafting had now gone leaving the machine tools in the workshop to be placed wherever most convenient. Each tool could then have its own electric motor, the drive being conveyed by flat, round or V-belting. As this arrangement applied also to the grinder a number of small grinding heads were produced that could be driven independently. A typical example is illustrated in *Fig. 3.2*. This grinder had plain cast-iron bearings, no bad thing this in machines designed for intermittent duty. As will be seen the driving pulley could accommodate either flat or round leather belting with the driving motor located at some convenient point adjacent to the machine.

Perhaps the motor is best sited below the bench if at all possible, for in this way it will be out of the way and largely protected.

An arrangement once used by a friend of the author's is depicted in *Fig. 3.4*. The motor itself sat on a cross member attached to the bench stretchers and was held down by a jacking system consisting of a shaped wooden block to which was fastened an electrical conduit flange. The conduit pipe seen in the illustration was made an easy screwed fit in the flange and had its upper end abutting a metal plate secured to the underside of the bench itself. Turning the tommy bar set in the tube forced the wood block into firm contact with the motor and held it in place. The motor itself was positioned

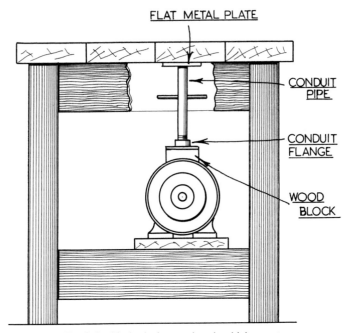

Fig. 3.4   Method of mounting the driving motor.

by a pair of dowels passing into holes drilled in its feet. The thinking behind the device envisaged the rapid removal of the motor for other purposes. History, however, does not suggest that this was a frequent requirement.

The motor was used to drive the gang of grinders illustrated in *Fig. 3.5*. These machines, between them, provided three grades of grit. The grinder at the back had a coarse wheel of 60 grit for

Fig. 3.5   A gang of small grinding heads.

Fig. 3.6 A simple single-wheel grinder.

rough grinding, the larger of the two machines in the front a No. 80 grit wheel for finishing purposes, while the small grinder, used for sharpening scribers, centre punches and the like, had a wheel of 120 grit. These two front machines are interchangeable for position and all have a type of tool rest that will be described later. These simply designed grinders are well depicted in *Fig. 3.6* illustrating the rear machine of the trio. It was contrived from a polishing head of French manufacture modified to accept a single wheel and provided with an outboard pulley. In this way the belt from the motor came up over the end of the bench. The machine was also used as a countershaft on the infrequent occasions when the smallest grinder needed to be driven.

Machine for Grinding on the Side of the Wheel

The equipment illustrated in *Fig. 3.7* was designed to take advantage of the benefits to be obtained from grinding tools on the side of the wheel. When one considers the effect of grinding on the wheel's periphery it will be clearly apparent that the curvature produced has a weakening effect on the tool's edge, and that the smaller the grinding wheel used the greater will be the ill effect.

When grinding on the wheel's face these ill effects will not be

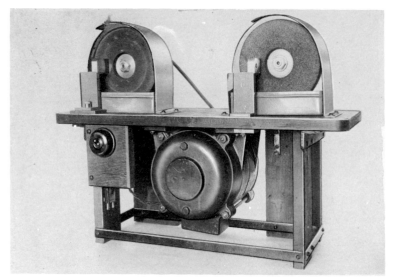

Fig. 3.7   Equipment for grinding on the side of the wheel.

Fig. 3.8   Driving side of the above equipment.

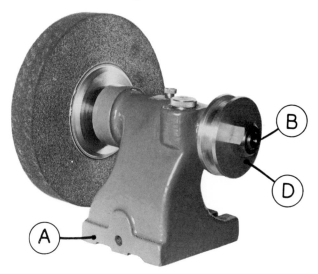

Fig. 3.9   One of the grinding heads.

present for all abrasion will take straight lines so no curvature will
be imparted to the tool's face.

The two grinding spindles were contrived from a pair of castings
originally intended for the making of lathe tailstocks, as may be
appreciated from a look at the illustration *Fig. 3.8* which depicts
the back of the grinding equipment.

As this type of grinding head is extremely rigid, it has been
suggested to the author that some readers would, perhaps, like to
make one or more of these heads. An enlarged view of the head,
therefore, is given in *Fig. 3.9*, together with a set of detailed drawings
including a sectional view *Fig. 3.10*. The details are given *Fig. 3.11*
to *Fig. 3.14*.

It is assumed that any reader contemplating the making of one of
these grinding heads will have sufficient practical knowledge to
carry out the work, so will need no formal instruction.

A word or two on matters of detail may not come amiss however.
First then, remember that the grinding wheel itself must have a
recess to accommodate the nut and flange securing the wheel on the
spindle, or the full face of the wheel will not be usable.

It should also be noted that the threads on the spindle 'B' must
be cut in the lathe, and the fixed flange screwed to it finally faced
when secured in place, the spindle being mounted between centres.
In this way the grinding wheel itself will run truly.

18

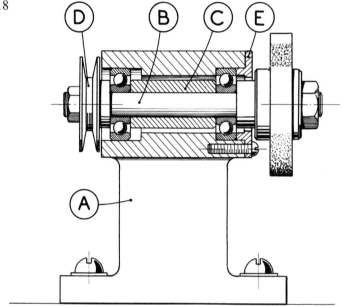

Fig. 3.10   Sectional view of the grinding head.

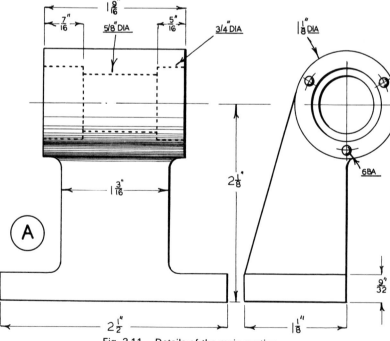

Fig. 3.11   Details of the main casting.

19

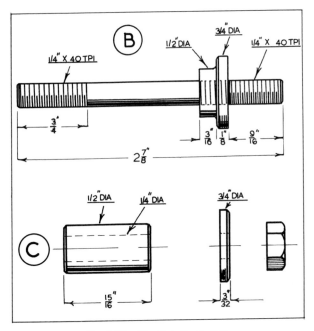

Fig. 3.12   The Spindle Details.

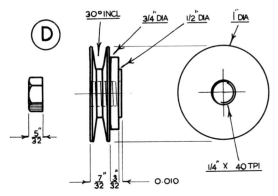

Fig. 3.13   Details of the Driving Pulley.

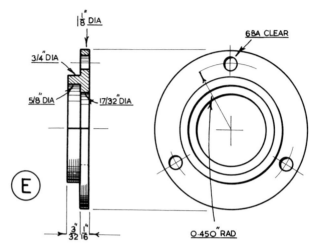

Fig. 3.14   Bearing Cover Plate details.

CHAPTER FOUR

ELECTRIC GRINDING MACHINES

For some years now doubled-ended electrically-powered grinding machines have been freely available to the amateur and to the user of the small workshop. These machines are based on grinders, large and small, that industry installs very widely. As a result there is now on the market a range of machines of proven reliability at a price that must commend them to anyone needing equipment of sound practical value.

The advent of the "Do-it-Yourself" cult has led to the production of many electric drills, some of which could be adapted for tool grinding. However, their use in this field smacks somewhat of improvisation, for in this way it is not possible to drive the size of wheel it would be safe to use at a speed that would assure satisfactory grinding.

Messrs. Black & Decker have appreciated that there was a lack of a suitable simple grinder that would appeal to the devotees of "Do-it-Yourself". Accordingly they have introduced their D370 5″ 127 mm. Bench Grinder, shown in *Fig. 4.1*. This is a machine intended for grinding on the rim of the wheel only, since a certain amount of spindle end float is provided for. Of the two wheels fitted one is coarse, about 60 grit, while the other is fine, 80 grit.

The wheel spindle is gear-driven from an electric motor built into the base of the machine. The motor is series-wound, so is suitable for either alternating or direct current at 230–250 volts. Obviously, this grinder is not silent in operation for the gears used and the speed at which they run can hardly be expected to contribute much to silence.

We come, now, to some of the larger grinding machines made by Black & Decker. The first of these is the 6″ (150 mm.) Bench Grinder, Ref. No. HD 1245. This machine has been designed for amateur and small workshop requirements. It can accommodate a pair of grinding wheels, but is supplied normally with a single

Fig. 4.1   The Black & Decker 5″ Bench Grinder.

Fig. 4.2   The Black & Decker 6″ Bench Grinder.

medium grit wheel at one end of the spindle and a wire bush at the other as may be seen in the illustration *Fig. 4.2*. The grinder in question is also of interest industrially as may be inferred from the range of standard voltages available:—

Single Phase A.C. 110–115 volts
            220–240 volts   50 & 60 cycles A.C.

Three Phase A.C. 220 – volts
             380 – volts
             440 – volts   50 & 60 cycles A.C.
             550 – volts

This machine is suitable for wheels 6″ diameter × $\frac{5}{8}$″ wide with $\frac{1}{2}$″ diameter spindle hole.

Fig. 4.3   The Black & Decker 7″ Bench Grinder.

Black & Decker 7″ Bench Grinder Ref. No. SDO 130

This grinder illustrated in *Fig. 4.3*, is next in size on Black & Decker's list. It is described by its makers as suitable for the medium sized tool room or engineering works. The $\frac{1}{3}$ h.p. motor powering the grinder can be supplied for the varying voltages and electrical power supplies already mentioned in connection with the 6″ machine, supplies that are usable with all the other grinders to be listed.

The no load spindle speed of the SDO 130 machine is 3000 r.p.m. and the wheels fitted 7″ by $\frac{5}{8}$″ by $\frac{1}{2}$″.

Black & Decker HD 1247 8″ Bench Grinder

This is a more powerful machine than the grinder just described. It has a one-half horsepower motor and is fitted with two 8″ by $\frac{7}{8}$″ × $\frac{5}{8}$″ wheels. Eye-shields are available and these may be attached to the brackets seen in *Fig. 4.4* fixed to the top of the wheel hoods.

Fig. 4.4   The Black & Decker 8″ Bench Grinder.

The Wolf range of Bench Grinders

Wolf Electric Tools Ltd. of Hanger Lane, London, W.5 market two bench grinders that are suitable for use in any workshop where off-hand grinding is practised. The smaller of them the 6″ (152 mm.) model 8681, is supplied with adjustable wheel guards and tool rests together with eye-shields providing complete protection for the operator. These details may be seen in the illustration *Fig. 4.5*.

The larger of the two machines, the 8″ (203 mm.) Model 8726 has exactly the same equipment as may be observed in the illustration *Fig. 4.6*. Both tools are furnished with a pair of grinding wheels, one coarse, one fine and both are available with motors suitable for either single or 3-phase electrical supply. The standard windings are:—

Single Phase 105/130 v. 200/240 v. 50 cycles A.C.
Three Phase 380/440 v. 50 cycles A.C.

For those who prefer to site their grinding machines away from the bench, and out of range of machine tools that might be harmed

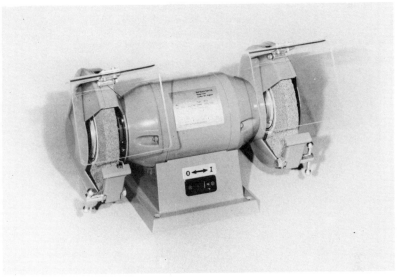

Fig. 4.5   The Wolf 6″ Bench Grinder.

Fig. 4.6   The Wolf 8″ Bench Grinder.

by the abrasive dust produced during wheel truing, a fabricated
pedestal No. 0602, is available. This will accept either of the two
machines mentioned, the mounting plate being drilled to suit both
grinders. The pedestal is illustrated in *Fig. 4.7.*

Fig. 4.7
The Wolf Grinder
on its floor
mounting.

CHAPTER FIVE

THE ANGULAR GRINDING REST

IN ORDER TO OBTAIN the best results from lathe and shaping machine tools, their cutting edges have to be ground to definite angles. For the most part this work is carried out free hand, the operator having to make a guess at the angles he needs to produce. This often involves both a waste of time and the material of which the tool itself is composed.

In industry, apart from tools tipped with Tungsten Carbide, grinding takes place on the *front* of the wheel. The grinders available to the Amateur and Small workshop, for the most part, have wheels 6″ diameter or less. These grind a hollow below the cutting edge which weakens it and lowers the tool's life between grinds. The effect of using a small wheel is depicted in *Fig. 5.1*. When the effect illustrated is augmented by a hollow ground top rake the resulting cutting edge is weak indeed, as may be inferred by observation of the dotted lines depicting the top rake.

For this reason the user of small grinders, having wheels 6″ diameter and under, is best served by grinding on the *side* of the wheel. In this position the faces ground on the tool itself are flat. The angular grinding rest enables tools to be ground in this way,

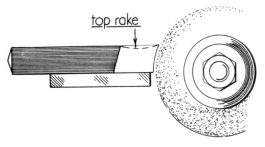

Fig. 5.1   Effect on tool of using a small grinding wheel.

27

with the added advantage that the rest can be set at the tool angle required. This also assists re-grinding since the angle is maintained so the time taken, and the stock removal needed to produce a fresh edge to the tool, is reduced to the minimum.

An example of a turning tool needing precise angular formation is the parting tool illustrated in *Fig. 5.2*. The angles involved are the Front Clearance 'A', the Side Clearance 'B', and the Relief Angles 'C' behind the cutting edge. The angles 'A' and 'B' are obtained by adjusting the grinding rest, whilst the angles 'C', not particularly critical ones, are obtained by swinging the tool on the rest.

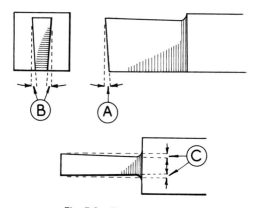

Fig. 5.2   The Parting Tool.

Grinding the Knife Tool will serve to demonstrate the method of using the angular rest. In *Fig. 5.3*, the tool is seen in section as viewed end-on from its shank. In this diagram a simple angle gauge is seen set on the tool rest so that, by bringing the edge of the gauge into contact with the side of the wheel, the rest can be set to the required angle.

The method should be clear from the diagram, but to avoid any ambiguity the terms "side clearance" and "side rake", as applied to the Knife tool, are shown in *Fig. 5.4*.

The Angle Gauge

The gauge used to set the rest consists of a piece of plate, brass or steel, fixed in a base. The blade of the gauge is filed off to the angles required, these angles being imparted with reference to the base

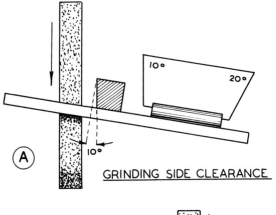

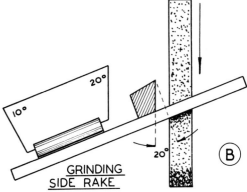

Fig. 5.3   Grinding the Knife Tool.

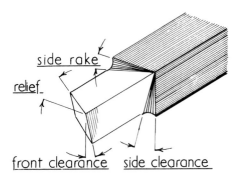

Fig. 5.4   Illustrating terms applied to tool grinding.

itself. The latter is most conveniently made from a piece of round material, filed or machined flat to provide an abutment face for the rest, and having a milled slot into which the blade is dropped and secured by sweating. The angles shown in the drawing are those most commonly needed; 10 degrees serving for Front Clearance, Side Clearance, and Side Rake needed on tools used when machining steel. Whilst 20 degrees of Side Rake is helpful when turning Aluminium alloys. However, as these gauges are easily made, a second example incorporating angles that practical experience has proved to be advantageous, may not come amiss.

Some Examples of the Angular Rest

The rest fitted to the miniature grinder illustrated in *Fig. 5.5* and *Fig. 5.6* will serve to demonstrate the basic design of the device. The title, "grinder" is, perhaps, inappropriate here, for the device is really a rotary hone intended for sharpening surgical instruments.

The rest has three main elements. These are the Base, the Column and the Table. The table is adjustable for height as well as for angle, both requirements being controlled by the clamp set at the top of the column. The clamp itself is similar to those fitted on surface gauges to secure either the column of the gauge or the scriber used with it.

Fig. 5.5   Miniature Grinder fitted with the angular rest.

Fig. 5.6   Miniature Grinder fitted with the angular rest.

A Simple Angular Rest

The rest illustrated in *Fig. 5.7* and in detail in *Fig. 5.8*, was made to test out the general acceptability of the device in a large machine shop. The simple parts were made from angle steel and were provided with sufficient means of adjustment to allow the angular rest to be used with the variety of electric grinders installed in the shop. The table 'A' was slotted to admit a one-inch wide grinding wheel, and stop pins were fitted to the Base 'B' to limit the angular movement of the Table. The Base itself was slotted to allow it to be adjusted for position. In this way the Table could be brought into the correct alignment in relation to the grinding wheel. The grinder illustrated in *Fig. 5.9*, was made from some redundant drilling machine castings in order to provide means of rough grinding tungsten carbide tipped tools. The work rest, depicted in *Fig. 5.10*,

32

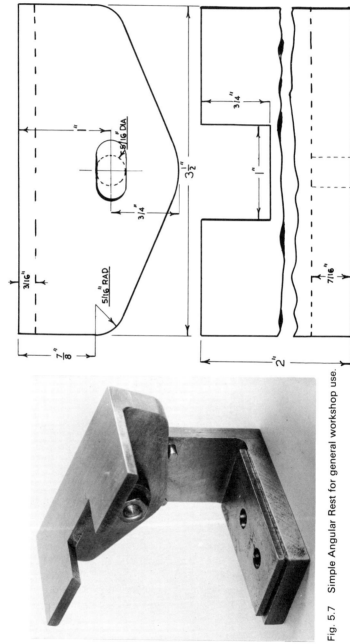

Fig. 5.7   Simple Angular Rest for general workshop use.

33

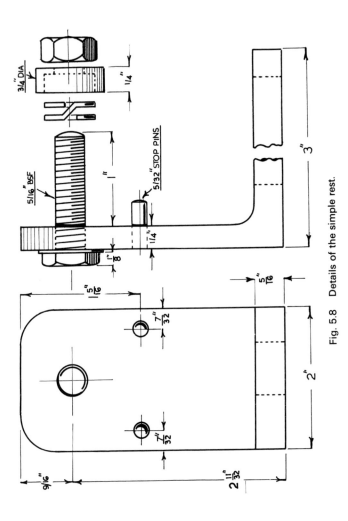

3/4" DIA

1/4"

5/16" BSF

1"

5/32 STOP PINS

1/4"

1/8"

1 5/16"

7/32"

7/32"

9/16"

5/16"

2"

2 11/32"

3"

Fig. 5.8   Details of the simple rest.

Fig. 5.9   Grinder made from surplus drilling machine castings.

Fig. 5.10   Work rest for the grinder depicted in Fig. 5.9.

consists of three main assemblies: The Soleplate (J), the Bracket (K) and the Table (L) attached to an Angle plate (L1). The Soleplate is slotted enabling the rest to be moved bodily in relation to the grinding wheel itself. The Bracket can be adjusted both sideways and radially in order to allow the rest to clear the wheel when the Table is tilted.

It has been suggested that the constructional details of the complete machine might be of interest to some readers so these together with details of the rest will be given in a later chapter.

Grinding Rests for the Commercial Twin Wheel Grinder

Commercial grinding machines, as befits their maker's desire to provide good value for money, usually have only very simple grinding rests. However, a little ingenuity, and really not a lot of labour, will finish these machines with rests whose merits the author is continually preaching. The illustration *Fig. 5.11*, shows a Wolf Bench Grinder modified to accept a pair of angular rests, one of

Fig. 5.11   Wolf Bench Grinder with angular rest and twist drill jig.

Fig. 5.12
Wolf Bench Grinder
with drill jig replaced
by a second tool rest.

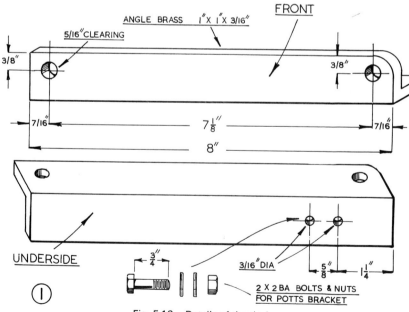

Fig. 5.13   Details of the tie-bar.

which can be removed so that a Potts Twist Drill Jig seen in the illustration can be fitted in its place. In *Fig. 5.12*, the second angular rest is depicted in place.

The basis of the fitting is a length of bright angle steel or brass attached to the original machine maker's rest anchorages. The relative parts are detailed in the illustrations *Figs. 5.13, 5.14, 5.15, 5.16, 5.17.*

Grinding the D-Bit

An example of the use of the Angular Rest for grinding specialist tools is depicted in *Fig. 5.18* and *Fig. 5.19*. The first of the two

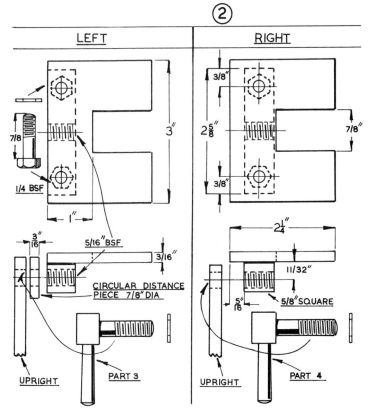

Fig. 5.14   The Rests.

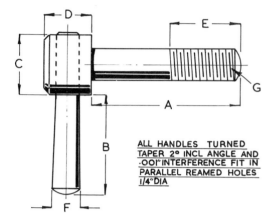

ALL HANDLES TURNED
TAPER 2° INCL ANGLE AND
·OOI″ INTERFERENCE FIT IN
PARALLEL REAMED HOLES
1/4″ DIA

PART No	A	B	C	D	E	F	G
③	$1\frac{1}{8}''$	$1\frac{1}{4}''$	5/8″	1/2″	3/4″	5/16″	5/16″ BSF
④	$1\frac{5}{16}''$	$1\frac{1}{4}''$	5/8″	1/2″	3/4″	5/16″	5/16″ BSF
⑥	7/8″	2″	5/8″	1/2″	1/2″	5/16″	5/16″ BSF

Fig. 5.15   Details of the locking handles.

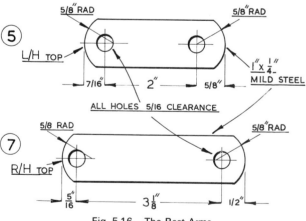

Fig. 5.16   The Rest Arms.

39

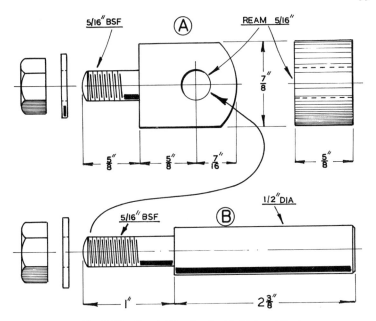

Fig. 5.17   Special Bracket for Right-hand Rest.

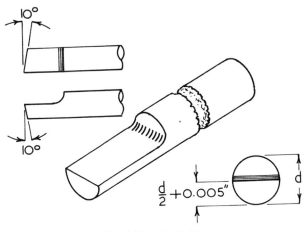

Fig. 5.18   The D-Bit.

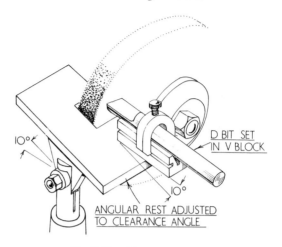

10°

D BIT SET
IN V BLOCK

10°

ANGULAR REST ADJUSTED
TO CLEARANCE ANGLE

Fig. 5.19   Grinding the D-bit.

illustrations shows the features of the D-bit, a tool used for drilling deep holes that are both straight and true to size. As will be seen two angles are involved, which may be imparted to the tool by using the rest in the manner depicted by the second illustration.

The form of angular rest shown, is one fitted to the grinder in the author's workshop; this has a table set in an upright member provided with a clamping device enabling the table to be tilted and locked at any desired point. The tongue that engages the upright is engraved with a scale of degrees from zero to 30 degrees each side of the zero point.

Front clearance for the D-bit is obtained by tilting the rest 10 degrees as shown in the diagram, whilst the front relief is imparted by swinging the tool sideways the same amount. In order to achieve a uniform finish to the grinding the tool is mounted in a V-block to which it must be firmly clamped. A line scribed on the work table will serve as a guide, or, alternatively, a simple fence consisting of a strip of metal, can be clamped to the table at the desired angle.

CHAPTER SIX

GRINDING TWIST DRILLS

IT IS GENERALLY ACCEPTED that an accurately ground drill is essential to the rapid production of correctly machined work. Commercial undertakings usually provide organisation that will ensure that the drills they use are properly serviced; so departments are set up, with equipment and personnel, to deal with the twist drill sharpening in bulk. For the most part, these departments only deal with drills above $\frac{1}{8}''$ diameter though, of course, engineering concerns whose work in the main involves the use of drills below this size set up apparatus to handle them.

In the amateur field and often in the small commercial workshop, while there are simple fixtures available that will assure accurate grinding, the operative has, for the most, to rely on freehand methods. These are matters that will be dealt with later, since, for some purposes an acceptably sharpened drill point can be produced freehand if the requirements and the problems involved are properly appreciated.

The Elements of the Drill Point

In order to understand what is required when sharpening a drill it is important to consider the make-up of the drill point.

The salient features are illustrated in *Fig. 6.1.* (A) is the point angle, commonly made 118° though other values are sometimes used. Clearance has also to be given behind the lips "a" "a" or the drill will not cut. This angle is denoted by the letter (B) and is usually about 10–12 degrees. In addition to imparting these angles accurately when grinding the lips must be made of equal length or the drill will cut oversize, as depicted in *Fig. 6.2.*

The chisel edge formed at the point of the drill must be kept as small as possible or it will slow down the drill's rate of cutting. The

41

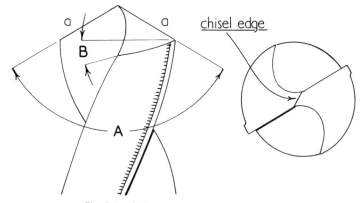

Fig. 6.1   Salient features of the Twist Drill.

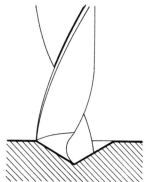

Fig. 6.2   Effect of an incorrectly formed drill point.

reason that this is so stems from the rubbing as opposed to the cutting action the chisel edge possesses. In large drills this rubbing action is considerable and sometimes needs to be reduced by "thinning" the drill point.

The thinning only extends for a short way down the flute of the drill and is commonly carried out freehand on a wheel with a curved rim. The effect of the point thinning depicted in *Fig. 6.3* at 'B' is also seen at 'C' where the effect on the drill point seen in elevation is illustrated.

Drill manufacturers stress the need to keep the web as narrow as possible. In this connection it must be remembered that, for reasons of strength, the web itself gets thicker the farther up the drill one proceeds. The table appended gives optimum value for web thickness, and it will have been apparent that this is a matter that has a direct bearing on the length of the chisel edge itself.

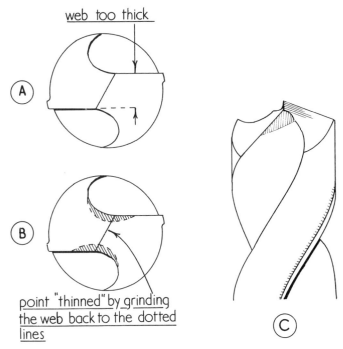

web too thick

(A)

(B)

point "thinned" by grinding
the web back to the dotted
lines

(C)

Fig. 6.3 "Thinning" The Drill Point A B & C.

The table has been produced by the Carborundum Company
Ltd., of Trafford Park, Manchester and is included in their treatise
"Tool Room Grinding", to which the author is indebted.

Diameter	Web Thickness	Diameter	Web Thickness	Diameter	Web Thickness
$\frac{1}{4}$	.040″	9/16	.078″	7/8	.110″
9/32	.043″	19/32	.078″	29/32	.113″
5/16	.047″	5/8	.082″	15/16	.117″
11/32	.050″	21/32	.085″	31/32	.120″
3/8	.054″	11/16	.089″	1	.124″
13/32	.061″	23/32	.092″		
7/16	.064″	3/4	.096″		
15/32	.068″	25/32	.099″		
1/2	.071″	13/16	.103″		
17/32	.075″	27/32	.106″		

An Alternative Method of Point Thinning

The somewhat negative action of the chisel edge has already been considered. An improvement however, is possible by making a radical alteration to the form of the chisel edge itself, converting it from a region virtually unable to do any cutting into one that will cut freely. This alteration has resulted from research and work connected with the accurate drilling of deep holes in high-tensile steels carried out by the author and others some years ago.

The thinking behind the research suggested that by making the chisel edge cut, and also act as a pilot drill, the drill loading itself would be reduced, the cutting as a whole would be freer and the drill life between grinds materially extended.

The modification to the chisel edge is depicted diagramatically in *Fig. 6.4.*

In this illustration (A) represents the normal chisel edge, (B) the Chisel Edge partly modified by grinding using a dish wheel and (C) finally modified to provide a pair of chisel edges at 180° to each other.

This modification is applicable to drills from $\frac{1}{4}''$ diameter upwards and can be imparted freehand provided one has a steady hand. However, the work is best carried out in a simple cutter grinder

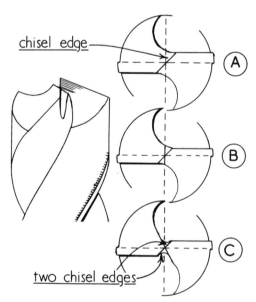

Fig. 6.4   Alternative method of thinning the drill point.

where the depth of grinding and the indexing of the work can be controlled.

The Twist Drill Grinding Jig

The somewhat complex nature of the drill point makes it imperative to use a grinding jig if drills are to be sharpened correctly.

From the description given of the rather complicated shape of the drill point, it will be clear that free-hand grinding is most unlikely to result in grinding the drill correctly; nevertheless, some workers with long practice become surprisingly adept. In "Model Engineer" of August 1913 Mr. L. A. Van Royen gave a detailed mathematical analysis of the constructional requirements for a twist drill grinding jig, and any pertinent information therein has been freely used. However, an operator with very little skill can grind a drill on a well-made jig with great accuracy.

Principles of Construction

At this stage, reference will be made to Van Royen's article for the geometrical construction of the jig necessary to form the correct back-off at the drill point. If, as represented in *Fig. 6.5*, the drill is

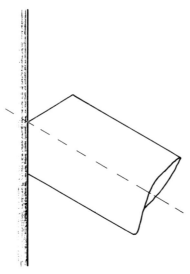

Fig. 6.5   Effect of rotating a drill on its axis against the wheel.

merely rotated on its axis while in contact with the grinding wheel, the point will take the form of a cone having an axis common to the drill axis. In *Fig. 6.6*, 'AB' is the drill axis and 'OC' is the axis on which the drill is made to turn, and it follows that the nearer the point 'A' is to the apex of the cone at 'O', the steeper will be the curvature of the back-off imparted to the drill point. Van Royen states that good results are obtained when the value of the cone angle at 'O' is made 26° and, at the same time, the distance from the apex of this angle to the drill axis is made equal to three times the diameter of the drill. As shown in *Fig. 6.7*, reproduced in a modified form from the Van Royen article, this distance is varied in accordance with the drill's diameter by bringing the drill point in advance of the pivoting axis for a distance equal to 1.4 times the drill's diameter. In this way the back-off suitable for a drill of any particular size can be obtained by adjusting the setting of the jig.

In addition, this writer states that the drill axis must be displaced to the right of the cone axis for a distance equal to 1/13 of the diameter of the drill. The drawing of the grinding jig described by Van Royen has been reproduced in *Fig. 6.8* in almost its original form, and the same principles of construction are still embodied in modern appliances.

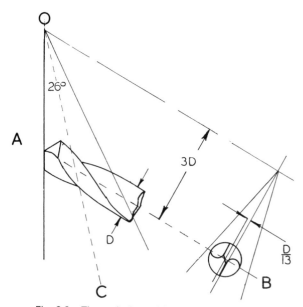

Fig. 6.6   Theoretical considerations of the drill jig.

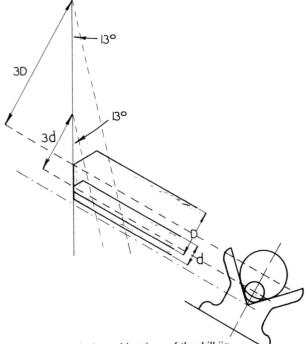

Fig. 6.7   Theoretical considerations of the drill jig.

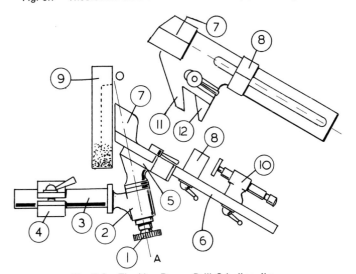

Fig. 6.8   The Van Royen Drill Grinding Jig.

The main pivot (1) of the jig rotates on the axis 'OA' in the bracket (2) attached to the sliding shaft (3) that, in turn, is clamped to the base bracket (4). The table (5) secured to the upper end of the pivot, carries the sliding drill carriage (6). The drill while being ground rests in the two V-blocks (7) and (8) and can be fed forward against the grinding wheel by means of the tailstock (10). To set the drill for the grinding operation, the main pivot is moved away from the wheel by sliding the shaft (3) in the bracket (4), and the correct position of the drill carriage in relation to the pivot axis is then set by closing the caliper jaws (11) and (12) on the shank of the drill which serves as a setting gauge.

After the jig itself has been slid forward to bring the front V-block just clear of the wheel, the drill is placed in position resting against the lip gauge, illustrated in *Fig. 6.9* and the appliance is then automatically set for grinding the drill correctly. This then is briefly the way the jig operates.

Of the jigs operating on this principle that are available to the amateur and to the small workshop two come to mind. The first of these is the Potts jig made by E. Potts of Ruthin, Denbighshire. This device has already been illustrated in Chapter Five attached to the Bench Grinder seen in *Fig. 5.10* and it is now depicted in some detail in the illustration *Fig. 6.10* of this chapter.

The other or second jig is that designed by "Duplex" and published some years ago in "Model Engineer". Drawings for this device depicted in *Fig. 6.11*, are still available from the offices of that periodical. The grinder employed is illustrated in the sectional drawing *Fig. 6.12*.

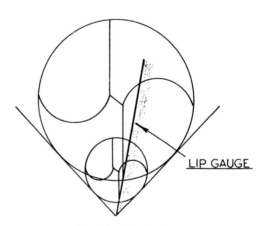

Fig. 6.9   The Lip Gauge.

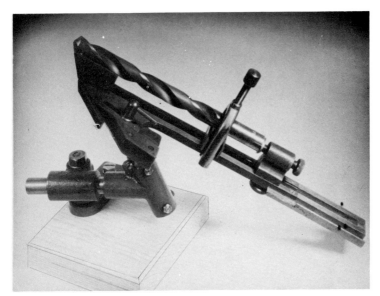

Fig. 6.10   The Potts Drill Grinding Jig.

Fig. 6.11   The Duplex Drill Grinding Jig.

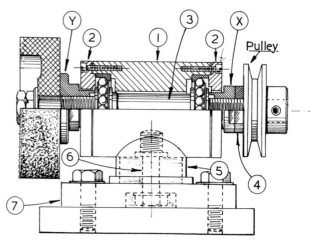

Fig. 6.12   Section of the Grinding Head.

The Grinding Wheel

The one fitted is of the form known as a cup wheel, which has the advantage that the working face is narrow and can readily be maintained in good condition when trued or dressed with a special tool. These wheels are $3''$ in diameter, $\frac{1}{2}''$ wide on the working face and $\frac{7}{8}''$ in total thickness. The central recess is $\frac{1}{2}''$ in depth, leaving a backing of $\frac{3}{8}''$. The coarser wheel, of 80 grit size, is made of white Bauxilite, which is a refined form of aluminium oxide. This substance cuts freely, without causing overheating of the work, and, owing to its friability, has but little tendency to become glazed. The fine wheel has a grit size of 220 and is reserved for grinding batches of very small drills, but so far the coarser wheel has proved satisfactory for sharpening drills down to size No. 60. The wheels illustrated were obtained from the Universal Grinding Wheel Co. of Stafford. It is important to mount the wheel rigidly to abut against a fixed flange of a diameter equal to half that of the wheel itself. The clamp nut should be tightened just enough to give a secure frictional drive, and this will be enhanced by fitting soft paper washers between the wheel and the driving flanges.

It will be noted that a lock nut has been fitted to the spindle to ensure that the clamp nut does not loosen if, as sometimes happens, the grinding wheels tends to over-run when the driving motor is switched off. The guard normally fitted to grinding wheels, to protect the operator in the event of the wheel chipping or breaking, is not illustrated. For when a cup wheel is used, the operator faces the wheel and is not in the direct line of danger. Moreover, the grinding pressure applied to the amply-thick wheel face is very light. Nevertheless, if preferred, and to satisfy factory regulations, a guard can be easily fitted by bending to shape a length of flat mild steel, say $1\frac{1}{2}'' \times \frac{1}{8}''$ and securing the two ends to the steel baseplate of the jig.

Dressing the Grinding Wheel

This will be necessary if the working surface becomes worn and, in part, loses its cutting properties. This results from the abrasive grains becoming blunted and not being shed so as to expose fresh, sharp grains. When this happens, the wheel is liable to overheat the work and draw the temper of the drill.

To restore the cutting efficiency of the wheel, its surface must be broken up to remove the worn abrasive grains. For this operation a star-wheel dresser is commonly used, and is then supported by a suitable tool rest.

Using the Grinding Jig

The method of operating the jig to grind a drill is illustrated in the sequence of drawings in *Fig. 6.13*. The base bracket clamp screw is first slackened and the jig moved away from the wheel. After the drill slide clamp screw has been freed, the caliper jaws are set to grip the shank of the drill and the screw is again tightened. Next the jig is rotated to the left until checked by the stop mechanism at the base of the main pivot. While held in this position at an angle of 90° to the wheel face, the jig is moved forwards until a piece of shim material, some 10 thousands of an inch in thickness, is gripped between the drill guide and the face of the wheel. The base bracket clamp screw is then tightened. The stop plate (N) is set to make contact with the foot of the stop arm (M) and the holding screw is securely tightened. With the drill slide remaining at right angles to the wheel face, the locking screw of the pivot collar (I) is finally tightened. Before going further, it is advisable to check that the forward part of the jig swings clear of the wheel when rotated through an angle of 45°.

The setting of the pivot stop collar needs no subsequent alteration, and the drill slide stop plate requires adjustment only when the wheel gap becomes widened by wear or dressing of the wheel face.

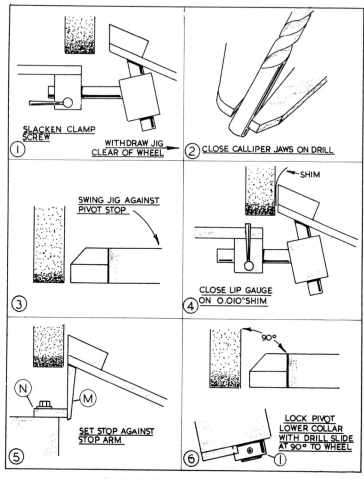

Fig. 6.13   Using the Grinding Jig.

With the drill placed in the two V-blocks, the tailstock is adjusted to bring the lower cutting lip against the lip guide, where it is held by firm finger pressure. After the grinder has been started, the drill is fed forward by means of the tailstock feed screw until the wheel begins to cut. The jig is then swung to the right with a steady, controlled movement until checked by the pivot stop.

On again swinging the jig to the left to the starting position, the drill is carefully raised from the V-guides and turned over so that it is again located by the lip gauge for grinding the other cutting edge.

Meanwhile, the setting of the feed screw remains unaltered. If care is taken, the two drill lips can be ground in this way without stopping the grinding wheel. When sharpening a drill, it is advisable to take light cuts alternately on the two lips, for a heavy cut is apt to draw the temper of the steel. It is important that the bearings of the grinding spindle should be accurately adjusted since any end-float may cause irregular grinding.

The angle of back-off given to the drill lips can, if required, be readily varied. If the caliper jaws are purposely set too far apart for the size of drill, the effect is to widen the base of the cone angle, represented by twice the angle formed between the axis of the main pivot and the face of the wheel. This lessens the curvature of the cone and so reduces the angle of back-off given to the drill point.

Conversely, if the caliper jaws are set closer than the diameter of the drill shank, the cone ground will have a short base radius and, as a result, a greater degree of curvature and back-off will be formed.

Freehand Drill Grinding

Early in this chapter the matter of freehand grinding was mentioned. While the inferiority of the process cannot be gainsaid, there are times when, for one reason or another, grinding without a jig is the only way possible.

The peculiarities of the drill point have already been considered so, if these are appreciated one can proceed to experiment preferably with an old drill of large size, since in this way it is easier to see what is going on and what errors are being made. A simple gauge will enable the point angle to be checked. This is made from a piece of steel plate filed to shape as depicted in *Fig. 6.14*.

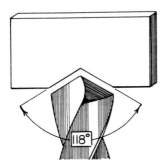

Fig. 6.14   Gauge for checking drill point angle.

In order to establish that both cutting edges are the same length another fixture can be employed. This device is also useful in checking the performance of a drill grinding jig. It will be seen, from observation of *Fig. 6.15*, that it consists of two major parts, a Base and a Vertical Member that can be used as a scribing point when the drill to be tested has the corners of its lips brought into contact with the surface which has previously been painted with blue marking fluid.

If the markings are as shown in the illustration the lips of the drill will be of unequal length and correction must be made by grinding until a line scribed by one drill lip is superimposed on a line marked by the other. Both lips will then be of equal length.

Backing-off, that is forming the relief behind the cutting edge, is a matter of grinding that needs some dexterity if it is to be carried out freehand. However, it is possible to train oneself in the correct movements using a stationary set-up to carry out a dummy run.

The set-up, as depicted in *Fig. 6.16*, consists of a large angle plate or a surface plate on edge, against which the drill is rolled as if being ground after the plate has been smeared with blue marking paste. A large drill should be used for the experiment, it will then be

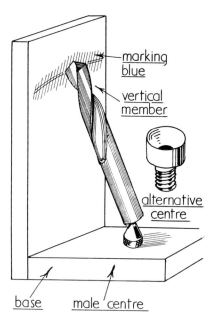

Fig. 6.15   Fixture for checking equality of lip length.

easier to observe how general is the blue marking on the drill thus
denoting the extent of the backing-off behind the cutting edges.

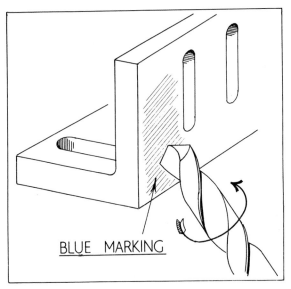

BLUE MARKING

Fig.　6.16　Simple set-up assessing movements needed when grinding a drill
freehand.

CHAPTER SEVEN

DRILL GRINDING HEAD

THE DRILL GRINDING HEAD, as illustrated in *Fig. 7.1*, is attached to the baseplate of the drill jig to form a unit which, in turn, is belt-driven by an electric motor mounted on a common baseboard. With this arrangement, a type of abrasive wheel best suited for drill grinding is used, and the complete assembly forms a compact machine always ready for immediate operation.

The Body—Fig. 7.1 Part 1

This was made from a short length of cored phosphor-bronze bar of the kind used for machining bearing bushes. Ordinary brass bar

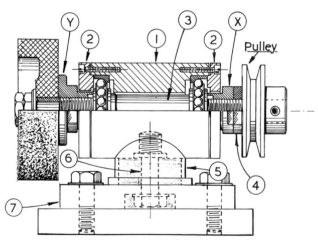

Fig. 7.1   Section of the Grinding Head.

56

will, however, be equally suitable. The material was turned parallel, the two ends were faced, and the bore was cleaned up to afford clearance for the machine spindle. A shank made from $\frac{3}{4}''$ square mild steel was screwed firmly into place against a shoulder formed in the body, where it was finally secured from turning by means of a taper pin. When fitting the shank to the body, the long axis of the head must be set parallel with the flat on the under side of the shank. This can readily be done on the surface plate with the aid of the test indicator. The purpose of the shank is to provide a means of gripping the work at centre height in the lathe toolpost. In any case, the body has to be drilled and tapped for the screw that attaches it to its baseplate. The alternative method of mounting the body for machining is to secure it directly to the lathe boring table in correct alignment.

With the shank gripped in the toolpost, the work was set at centre height with the aid of the test indicator, mounted in the lathe chuck and rotated slowly by hand. The body was set parallel with the lathe axis by means of a try-square held against the chuck face. The final, correct alignment was obtained by adjusting the cross-slide until test indicator readings, taken at intervals of 90° were found to be identical.

With the work accurately set, the housings for the ball bearings were machined with a boring bar running between the lathe centres. For the boring operation it will be found more convenient to use a bar carrying two cutter bits, spaced apart an inch or so more than the overall length of the body. When the first housing is nearing its finished size, a reading is taken with the test indicator against the cutting edge of the tool.

For this purpose, the test indicator was mounted on the pillar of the surface gauge with its base resting on the lathe bed. To locate the indicator, the register pegs in the base of the gauge were extended to make contact with the guide surface of the lathe bed shears. By taking a micrometer reading in the housing, or by transferring a caliper measurement, the tool can be set with the aid of the test indicator to machine the housing to the finished size. Furthermore, by moving the test indicator along the lathe bed, the other cutter-bit can finally be set to machine the second bearing housing to the same size as the first. Both ends of the body should be faced square with the housings, by taking a light scraping cut with each tool-bit in turn, before the work is removed from the lathe.

The housings should be made a light push fit for the bearings, for any tendency on the part of the outer ball races to rotate is checked by the pressure plates fitted at either end of the body. Remember that, as represented in *Fig. 7.2*, the two ends of the central bore in the body must be enlarged to enable the outer races to be withdrawn when required.

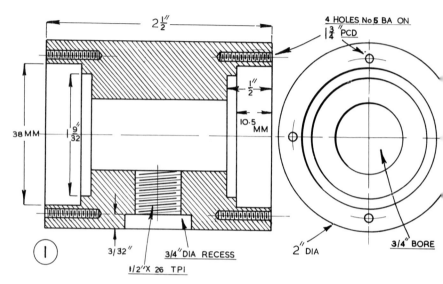

Fig. 7.2   The Body.

The Ball Bearings

Those chosen were a pair of Hoffman magneto-type bearings No. A16, having an outside diameter of 38 mm. and a bore of 16 mm. These, the manufacturers state, are suitable for light radial and thrust loads and can be run at very high speeds. But it is important to ensure that the axial adjustment does not throw any permanent load on the balls. As shown in the accompanying drawings, the left-hand inner ball race is located by being securely clamped against a shoulder, but the corresponding right-hand race is made an accurate sliding fit on the spindle, so that the necessary adjustment can be made to eliminate end-float. To obtain a close sliding fit for the latter ball race, the spindle seating may, with advantage, be lapped to form a finished surface that should not suffer wear from dismantling the parts during the course of construction. On the other hand, any ridges left on a turned surface will eventually cause a slack fit if the crests become worn.

The End Plates—Fig. 7.1 Part 2

They serve to clamp the outer races of the bearings securely in their housings.

Although the machining is a straightforward turning operation, it is important to form the central bore truly concentric with the register shoulder. This permits a minimum working clearance for the spindle clamp collars to form an efficient grease and dust seal. The end plates are shown in the drawing as secured with four 5B.A. cheese-head screws; but, if preferred this number can be increased to six.

The Spindle Fig. 7.1 Part 3

This was machined from $\frac{3}{4}''$ diameter mild-steel rod, which was faced and centre-drilled at either end before being mounted between centres in the lathe. To ensure accuracy, it is advisable to screwcut the threaded ends of the spindle. The two small flats filed on the right-hand end of the spindle enable it to be securely gripped, either in the vice or by means of a spanner, when adjusting the bearings or clamping the grinding wheel in place.

The Bearing Clamp Collars Fig. 7.1 Part X and Y

These were machined from mild-steel rod. It is important that the internal threads should be accurately cut so that even contact is

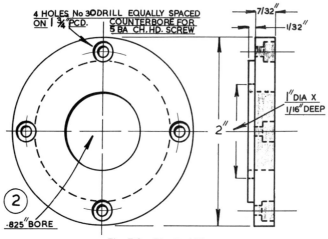

Fig. 7.3   The End Plates.

made against the inner bearing races. The left-hand collar is of larger diameter to provide an adequate clamping surface for the grinding wheel. Although this is not shown in the drawing, the face of the collar should be recessed at its centre to ensure an even bearing for the wheel. This also allows a light finishing cut to be taken over the actual abutment surface, with the collar securing the ball bearing in place and the spindle again mounted between centres.

The Grinding Wheel Bush

This fits closely on the end of the spindle, which is reduced to $\frac{3}{8}''$ diameter and threaded 26 t.p.i. The bush is turned to a close fit in the standard $\frac{1}{2}''$ diameter wheel bore, but without imposing any bursting strain on the wheel. The part can either be made parallel, as shown in the inset drawing in *Fig. 7.4*, or a flanged bushing can be employed.

Where both coarse and fine wheels are mounted separately on the spindle for grinding large and small drills, it may be better to fit the individual wheels with the flanged type of bush. This will prevent wear of the lead bushes fitted to the wheels, and consequent slackness in the mounting.

In case the reference to using both coarse and fine-grit wheels may lead to a misunderstanding, it should be pointed out that, in actual practice, a wheel of medium grit-size has been found satisfactory for grinding drills ranging from No. 60 to $\frac{5}{8}''$ diameter. But where small predominate, and larger drills are only occasionally ground, the use of wheels of two different types may be found an advantage. Particulars of these grinding wheels will be given later.

The Belt Pulley

This was machined from cast-iron rod, which is highly resistant to wear, but mild steel can be used for making the part if the better material is not available.

Aluminium pulleys of this small size are apt to become polished and worn in the V-groove, leading to belt slip. The pulley is necessarily of small diameter to avoid having to fit the driving motor with an unduly large belt pulley in order to obtain the correct speed for the grinding wheel. The pulley groove was machined with a form tool to an included angle of 30° to accommodate a V-belt, $\frac{1}{4}''$ in width and $\frac{3}{16}''$ in thickness.

The bore of the pulley was threaded $\frac{1}{2}'' \times 26$ t.p.i. to screw on to the spindle, where it was secured by a 2 B.A. Allen grub-screw,

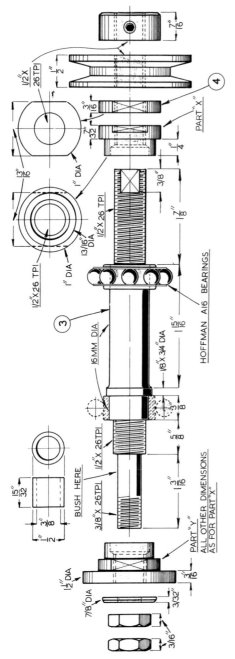

Fig. 1.4 The Spindle and the Grinding Wheel Bush.

inserted in the pulley boss. To protect the spindle threads, it is advisable to let the screw bear on a soft-metal pad.

This completes the essential work on the grinding head itself, but before final assembly the ball bearings should be lightly packed with thin grease of the kind produced for this purpose. Subsequent lubrication will not be needed for a long time, and when this is due the head can be dismantled for cleaning as well as for adding lubricant. As an alternative, greasing holes can be drilled in the end plates to allow a gun to be used for feeding the grease directly to the bearings. The grease-ways must, however, be closed with a grub-screw to prevent the entry of grit into the working parts.

As already pointed out, on no account must any permanent end-load be put on the bearings when adjusting the right-hand spindle collar. After the final adjustment has been made, and the locking collar securely tightened, the spindle should revolve freely and be just free from end-float and radial play.

To facilitate this operation, a small spanner was made to engage the flats formed on the spindle adjusting and locking collars. The material used should be rather better than ordinary mild steel, and carbon-steel strip will be found more suitable. When applying the spanner, in conjunction with an ordinary open-ended spanner, the spindle can be gripped by the two flats formed at its right-hand end.

The drawing *Fig. 7.1*, shows how the finished grinding head is mounted on a small baseplate (7) by means of a saddle (5) and a draw bolt (6). This assembly is, in turn, attached to the main baseplate of the jig by two $\frac{5}{16}''$ B.S.F. Hexagon-headed screws.

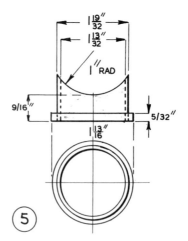

Fig. 7.5   The Saddle.

The Saddle Fig. 7.5

It can be made of brass and is either built up by hard-soldering a short length of thick-walled tubing into a turned collar, or as in the present instance, the plummer may be able to supply a suitable machined casting like that forming the waste-pipe joint of a wash basin. In either case, it will be necessary to form the hollow in which the body of the grinding head rests. This is, perhaps, best done by a machining operation in the lathe, for forming the contour accurately with hand tools is a somewhat difficult and tedious job. To carry out the machining of the saddle fitting, it was clamped to an angle plate with a backing of a piece of blotting paper, as shown in *Fig. 7.6*, and the finished depth of machining was indicated by a line scribed with the jenny calipers at a distance of $\frac{9}{16}''$ from the base.

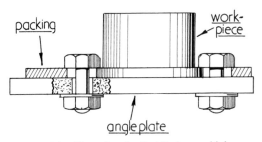

Fig. 7.6   Mounting the Saddle for machining.

The angle plate was bolted to the lathe boring table and set parallel with the lathe axis by means of a try-square held against the chuck face.

To set the centre line of the work at lathe centre height, the upper surface of the part was set for a distance equal to half its diameter above the point of the tailstock centre. A true running boring bar, fitted with an adjustable cutter bit, was mounted in the lathe, and the cutter was set to a radius of exactly $1''$ to correspond with that of the boring head body.

As the cutter bar measured $0.750''$ in diameter, the cutter was set to project a further $0.625''$ to equal the working radius of $1''$. This setting was carried out in the way represented in *Fig. 7.7*, with the test indicator mounted on the pillar of the surface gauge and set at lathe centre height. The indicator was located by the extended base pegs of the gauge bearing against one of the cross-slide T-slots. After bringing the anvil of the test indicator into contact with the boring bar, both the dial of the indicator and the cross-slide index

64

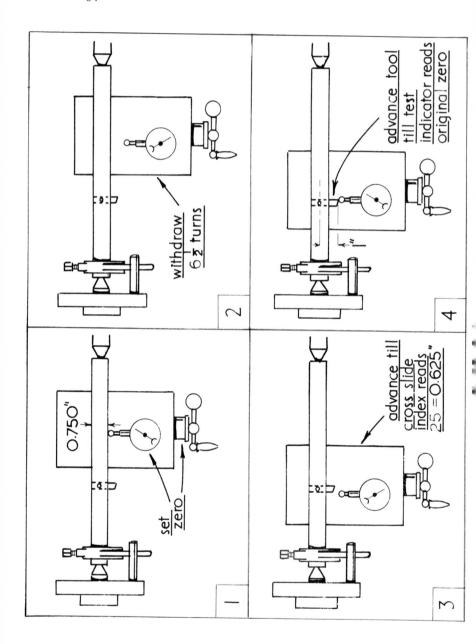

collar were set to zero. Following this, the 10 t.p.i. slide feed screw was turned back for six and a half turns and then fed forward to the 25 mark on the index collar. This gave a final setting of 0.625″ equal to the required projection of the cutter from the boring bar.

Finally, the cutter bit, when in contact with the indicator anvil, was adjusted to return the test indicator to the original zero reading. When making this adjustment the lathe mandrel should be turned by hand in the reverse direction, and the highest reading of the test indicator will then represent the cutting radius of the tool.

Although this may seem a lengthy and involved routine, in practice the tool-setting can be carried out quite quickly and with but little chance of error. Moreover, it should ensure an accurate result without having recourse to the more tedious process of working by trial and error.

With the set-up completed, it only remains to take a series of traversing cuts to machine the saddle concavity to the correct radius and to the full finished depth. Should any small correction, however, be found necessary, this can readily be made by using a triangular hand-scraper to remove any high spots, indicated by the transference of marking compound when the parts are mated. Even contact between the body and the saddle is essential to ensure working rigidity when the grinding jig is finally assembled.

The Holding-down Bolt Fig. 7.1 Part 6

It secures the body of the grinding head to its baseplate and is a straightforward turning and threading job. Turn the smaller diameter portion first and thread the end $\frac{3}{8}$″ B.S.F. from the tailstock. After parting off the bolt to length, reverse it in the chuck and finish the other end to the dimensions given in the drawing. The work can be held in the self-centring chuck for the latter operation, as exact concentricity is not essential. The stud should be checked to make sure that it is of the correct length and will not project beyond the under surface of the baseplate. An alternative, and more accurate, method of machining the part is to turn and screwcut it between centres in the lathe and, if necessary, the threaded portions can be finally sized with the corresponding dies.

The Baseplate—Part 7

This was made from a short length of $1\frac{7}{8}$″ × $\frac{1}{2}$″ flat, mild steel. The abutment surfaces should be trued either by filing or by machining

66   *The Grinding Machine*

in the lathe or shaping machine. The clearance-size holes for the two hexagon-headed fixing screws were spaced to correspond with the holes previously drilled and tapped in the baseplate of the jig itself. As shown in the drawing, the nut of the holding-down bolt lies in a recess formed in the under side of the grinding head baseplate. The diameter of this counterbore should be large enough to allow a $\frac{5}{16}''$ Whitworth box spanner to engage the $\frac{3}{8}''$ B.S.F. clamping nut. For forming the nut recess, the work was gripped in the four-jaw chuck, with the $\frac{3}{8}''$ diameter bolt hole set to run truly, and a small boring tool was used to machine the flat seating for the nut.

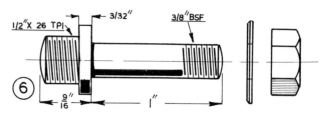

Fig. 7.8   The Holding-down Bolt.

CHAPTER EIGHT

GRINDING IN THE LATHE

THE PROCESS OF GRINDING in the lathe is sometimes a useful facility. Large industrial concerns generally have equipment in their tool stores that will permit this form of grinding to be carried out, and undoubtedly there are occasions when the equipment comes in useful.

The grinder used is mounted on the toolpost and, for the most part, is self-contained; that is the spindle and the motor that drives it are grouped together in an assembly that can be clamped to the top slide.

Many years ago the author, in "Model Engineer" published a series of articles describing the Toolpost Grinding Spindle used in his workshop. It is these articles that form the basis of what follows.

The Toolpost Grinder is an item of workshop equipment that often finds an application when it is available, but whose capital cost does not usually warrant its purchase, except, of course, in the hands of the professional user. It has been suggested, therefore, that a satisfactory machine, capable of being made in the small workshop, would be of interest to readers.

For the most part toolpost grinders, somewhat naturally, give the best results when used on large lathes where the machine slides are of robust proportions. However, if care is taken these grinders will produce good work on light lathes and we ourselves regularly use this type of equipment with a Myford ML7 lathe.

The device, seen in the illustrations, *Figs. 8.1* and *8.2* was originally intended as an aid to the sharpening of circular screwing dies, and as such was designed for internal grinding only. Its use for external grinding operations is therefore limited.

The grinding spindle accommodates mounted points; these are small grinding wheels permanently fixed to spindles that may be secured in the collet chuck with which the device is fitted. We shall have more to say on this subject later.

Fig. 8.1   The Toolpost Grinder.

Fig. 8.2   The Toolpost Grinder.

Toolpost Grinder

The Toolpost grinder consists of three major units. First, the Baseplate and Cradle for the Grinding Spindle, the Cradle being provided with an adjustment for spindle height. Secondly, the Grinding Spindle itself and lastly, the Motor and its mounting. We may as well dispose of this assembly straight away as it is somewhat specialised, the motor used having been obtained from Government disposal sources. Details of the motor may be of interest, however, in case some of these machines may still be available.

The motor is a low-voltage direct current machine capable of giving $\frac{1}{3}$ h.p. for short periods. It operates on 10–12 volts satisfactorily, and, being a series wound machine, may be run from the house mains provided that a transformer that will give a large enough output is available. In our own workshops the motor is usually fed from a rectifier as it will run cooler if supplied from a direct current source. The reason for this is that the field magnet cores are not laminated, so, when alternating current is used, the eddy currents in them are considerable. The heating effects of these eddy currents are great, thus materially increasing the temperature rise in the machine as a whole.

However, if used with discretion, these motors will be found quite a practical proposition. Their quality is of the highest and they could be bought at a figure that must have been but a small fraction of the original cost.

The rating plate on the machine bears the following information:—

| Rating | 2.5 mins. | H.P. 0.33 | r.p.m. 3500 |
| Volts | 24 d.c. | Amps 20.5 | Type A20/S31 |

These machines are compound wound and should be left so if they are to be used on direct current always. However, if alternating current is to be employed the compound turns may be isolated or reconnected to allow the machine as a whole to be re-wired as a series wound machine.

The Driving Pulley fitted to the motor is 5″ diameter and drives on to a spindle pulley $\frac{3}{4}$″ diameter. At the rated speed for the motor of 3,500 r.p.m. this gives the grinder a spindle speed of approximately 23,000 r.p.m.

The Driving Belt

The driving belt used is a woven cotton belt impregnated with latex. The belt is, of course, endless since no joint can be permitted because this would interfere with the smooth running of the spindle. The belt is 26 inches in circumference and $\frac{1}{2}$″ wide.

We have tried both impregnated and plain cotton belts and have found the former type to be far superior since impregnated belts do not tend to stretch in the way plain belts do.

The Transformer

The transformer used should be capable of giving an output of 750 watts at 14–20 volts A.C. This rating was once a standard for Service requirements. The connecting leads should be capable of dealing with current densities up to 30 amperes.

The Motor Mounting

The motor mounting is a simple angle plate bored to accommodate the spigot and flange of the motor itself. This mounting bolts to the grinder baseplate, upon which it can slide to tension the belt, and is controlled by two knurled jacking screws. It is, of course, possible to employ motors normally designed for operation direct from the mains; these will need a mounting to suit individual cases.

The Spindle

The spindle, illustrated in *Fig. 8.3* and in section in *Fig. 8.4*, was originally designed to carry its grinding wheel in a collet close to the bearing assembly. It has since been fitted with an extension spindle enabling deeper internal grinding to be carried out.

The assembly consists of a body (A), machined from mild-steel bar, fitted with a pair of labyrinth end caps (B) designed to secure the bearings in place and keep out dust. Two lubricators (C) are provided to conduct oil directly to the ball races.

Fig. 8.3   The Grinding Spindle.

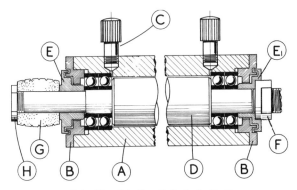

Fig. 8.4   The Grinding Spindle in Section.

The Wheel Arbor (D) is machined from a piece of high-tensile steel such as an old side-shaft from a motor car. The Arbor is deliberately increased in diameter between the bearing seatings in order to minimise vibration, an important factor in promoting good work finish.

Two End-Caps (E) and (E1), registering with the body end-caps, in addition to keeping out dirt serve to secure the inner faces of the bearings through the medium of the nuts (F) and (H); the latter also secures the Pulley (G).

The Collets

The collet arrangements are simple as may be seen in the scrap section *Fig. 8.5.* They consist of the Collet Closing Nut (J) and the Collet (K) housed in the spindle itself. This method was found adequate for the original purposes of the grinding spindle, but later it was found desirable to make provision for grinding to a greater

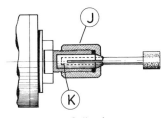

Fig. 8.5   The Collet Arrangements.

depth, so the Extension seen in the illustration *Fig. 8.6* was added. This extension screws directly on to the spindle nose in place of the collet closing nut (J) and is provided with its own collet and nut, the collet itself being made integrally with the extension spindle.

The Spindle Pulley (G)

At the opposite end of the spindle to the collet is the Spindle Pulley. This part was made from Tufnol, a cotton based plastic material; the details are seen in the illustration *Fig. 8.7*. Also in the same illustration details are given of the Spindle Nut (F) and the Pulley Nut (H). The pulley is not keyed to the spindle, but is made a good fit upon it and held against the outer face of the Inner Bearing Cap (E) by means of the pulley nut. The pulley is slightly crowned and has radial grooves designed to spill air trapped under the belt when the grinder is running.

The Collet Chuck

The Collet Chuck (K) and its attendant Closer (J) are seen in the illustrations whilst the details of these parts are given in *Fig. 8.8*.

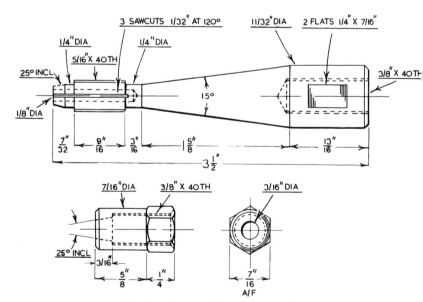

Fig. 8.6   Details of the extension spindle.

So far as the collet is concerned all the turning can be carried out at the same setting, as can also the machining of the three 0.020″ slots provided a lathe milling attachment is available. This operation is illustrated in *Fig. 8.9*. When producing the $\frac{1}{8}$″ bore, provided that the alignment of the lathe tailstock and headstock are above re-

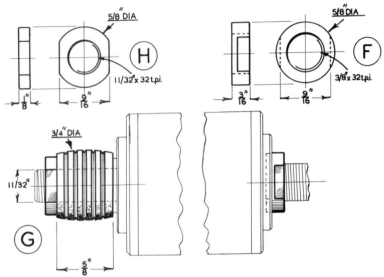

Fig. 8.7   Details of the Pulley (G), the Pulley Nut (H) and the Spindle Nut (F).

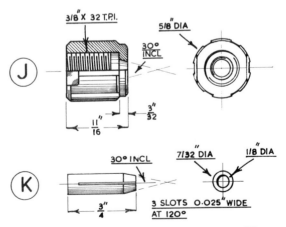

Fig. 8.8   Details of the Collet (K) and Closer (J).

Fig. 8.9   Machining the slots in the collet.

proach, it will be in order, first, to centre drill the work, following this by a No. 31 drill. A $\frac{1}{8}''$ reamer can then be used to size the hole.

Making the Closer is largely a single-setting operation. Again accuracy is essential, but the part should be made an easy fit on the spindle so that the closer can engage the nose of the collet without the possibility of the latter being pulled out of alignment.

The Bearings

The Bearing layout is of simple design, again in view of the original requirements, and is as seen in the sectional illustration, *Fig. 8.4* given earlier. The ball races used are of deep-groove type $\frac{7}{8}''$ diameter $\times \frac{3}{8}''$ bore $\times \frac{7}{32}''$ wide. A better arrangement, perhaps, would be to introduce a pair of angular contact races at the working end of the spindle. In this way some slight provision for pre-loading could be obtained with the added facility of taking up wear when needed. However, it must be said that, despite many hours of work, the present bearing assemblies are standing up well and show no signs of requiring replacement.

Baseplate and Spindle Mounting

The Baseplate (A), illustrated in *Fig. 8.10* and in detail in *Fig. 8.11*, is made from a piece of bright mild-steel plate and clamps to the lathe top-slide using the toolpost stud and nut for the purpose. The forward end of the plate is provided with a boss screwed and brazed to it in order to act as a hinge for the spindle mounting.

This hinge consists of two cradles B and C that can be locked to the baseplate by means of the lockscrew (D). A height adjustment mechanism is attached to the left-hand cradle consisting of an operating lever (E) controlled by the knurled screw (F) turning in the trunnion (H) and imparting movement to the lever by means of the nut (C). Both nut and trunnion are free to turn in the lever and baseplate respectively. When using the mechanism the cradle is first unlocked, the height adjustment made by turning the knurled screw and the cradle again locked before the grinding spindle is set in motion. The details of this mechanism are given in *Fig. 8.12*.

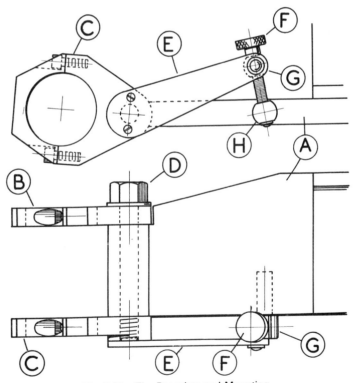

Fig. 8.10   The Baseplate and Mounting.

76

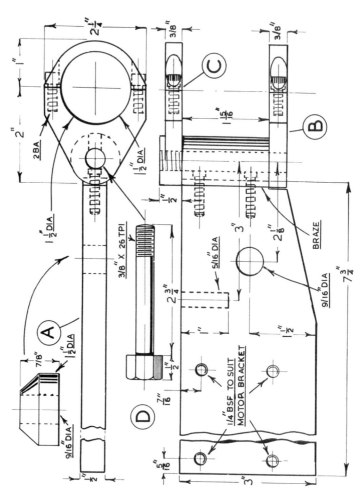

Fig. 8.11   Details of the Baseplate & Mounting.

77

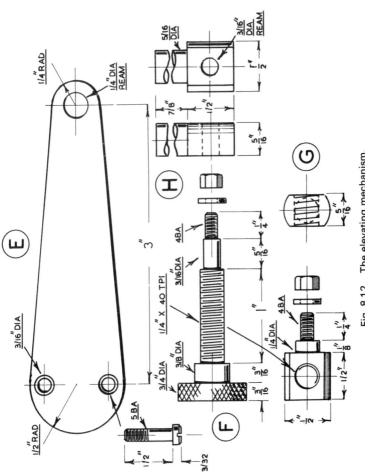

Fig. 8.12 The elevating mechanism.

Grinding Wheels and Mounts

We have already touched briefly on the subject of suitable grinding wheels, and have mentioned the mounted points with which the toolpost grinder is intended to be used.

Most well-known grinding wheel manufacturers supply mounted points and these may be obtained in a wide variety of shapes and sizes. The abrasive varies according to whether the work is hard or soft, and the wheel grit size is dictated largely by the size of the wheel itself. In this connection it should perhaps be added that a little thought will explain the difficulty of making very small compact wheels from a coarse grit abrasive material. We have already seen that an average spindle speed for the machine is of the order of 25,000 r.p.m. This is a makers recommended maximum speed for a wheel $\frac{7}{8}''$ diameter, but smaller wheels have been found to operate quite satisfactorily at this speed.

It is possible to raise the voltage applied to the driving motor and to control it by means of a variable resistance. In this way the range of wheel sizes used may be greatly increased.

Care of the Grinding Wheel

Much can be written about the treatment and servicing of grinding wheels. Indeed much has been written on the subject, this information being freely obtainable from the makers.

There are, however, a few salient points that need to be mentioned. In the first place the grinding wheel must run true. Failure to ensure that it does so will not only produce poor work but may materially lessen the life of the wheel. Secondly, a grinding wheel should never be crowded on to the work. Excessive pressure contributes nothing to the satisfactory working of the wheel. It usually promotes vibration so, as soon as this is experienced, the feed must be reduced immediately. As these are matters involving the correct use of the top-slide for setting the in-feed we shall return to this matter later.

Truing the Grinding Wheel

Before the grinder can be used the wheel or point must be trued. This is best carried out with a piece of coarse carborundum held lightly against the wheel as it is rotating. While this work is being performed the lathe slides must be well protected against abrasive dust that is formed during the operation. The carborundum slip, obtainable from the wheel manufacturers, should be held in such a way that the abrasive dust from the wheel discharges downwards. In this way airborne abrasive particles are reduced to a minimum.

For the most part the mounted points should be used dry. If any lubricant at all is used this should be water in which a small amount of washing soda has been dissolved. If a wheel has accidentally come into contact with lubricating oil it should be washed in petrol or trichlorethylene and left to dry before being used again.

Lubricating the Machine

The lubrication of the grinding spindle should be kept to a minimum. If the bearings are flooded with oil they will not operate freely and so the spindle may not rotate at its full speed. A light spindle oil should be used and the amount confined to a couple of drops in each bearing at very infrequent intervals.

The lubrication of the motor will depend on the class of machine fitted. The motor seen in the illustrations has its ball races packed with grease and has needed no attention for many years.

Using the Toolpost Grinder

We come now to the steps that must be taken when using the tool-post grinder. It will have already been noted that a fine in-feed is essential if the abrasive wheel is to do its work properly, and it will be further appreciated that the coarseness of the feed derived from the cross-slide alone renders its use quite inadequate. So, except as a means of roughly positioning the grinding wheel in relation to the work, the cross-slide must be ignored and firmly locked during grinding operations. Since we need the facility of feeding the wheel to the work in steps of a maximum of 0.0001″ at a time other means must be sought for achieving this end. In *Fig. 8.13* the solution is depicted.

If the top slide to which the toolpost grinder is attached is set over 6 degrees then a movement of 0.010″ as shown by the top slide feed screw index will result in an actual movement of 0.001″ by the grinding wheel towards the work. In other words every 0.001″ read on the index represents 0.0001″ of feed towards or away from the work depending upon which way the feed screw handle is turned.

With the toolpost grinder, small *external* grinding operations are possible provided that the longitudinal extent of the work is not great. Practical examples are lathe centres, centre punches and any work needing the formation of short cones.

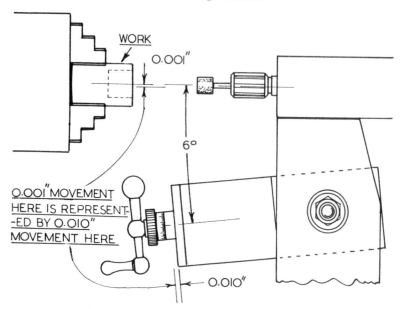

WORK

0.001"

6°

0.001" MOVEMENT
HERE IS REPRESENT-
-ED BY 0.010"
MOVEMENT HERE

0.010"

Fig. 8.13   Setting over the top slide to obtain a fine feed.

When grinding of this type is undertaken the top slide has to be set over the angle needed on the finished work. It follows, therefore, that the in-feed of the wheel has to be made by means of the cross-slide feed screw alone leaving the top-slide to move the grinding wheel across the work surface. This means that the cross-slide feed screw has to be used delicately. Here feeds of 0.0005 to 0.001" have been found suitable, and these are readily obtainable from a reading of the index, even with the small dials fitted to a number of lathes.

Mounted points serve well as the grinding media, but it is also possible to make for oneself arbors to take the small unmounted wheels that may be purchased. Two of these are seen in the illustration *Fig. 8.14* mounted on suitable arbors marked A and B respectively.

Also seen in the same illustration is an extension arbor for holding mounted points. This arbor is seen dismantled in the upper part of the illustration *Fig. 8.15* together with a mounted point and its attendant collet and closer for use at such times as it is desired to use the grinder without an extension. A list of NORTON Plain mounted Wheels and points is given in *Fig. 8.16*.

When making the arbors for unmounted wheels it is essential

Fig. 8.14   Small wheels and arbors for external grinding operations.

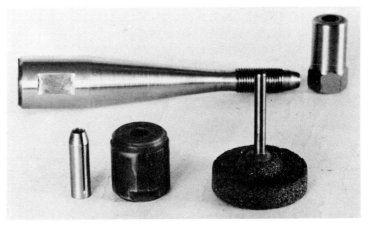

Fig. 8.15   The spindle extension and a mounted point for external grinding.

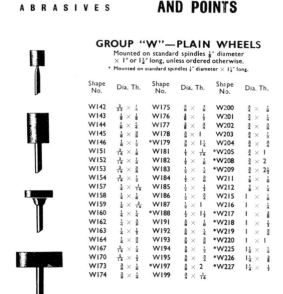

NORTON
A B R A S I V E S

MOUNTED WHEELS
AND POINTS

GROUP "W"—PLAIN WHEELS

Mounted on standard spindles $\frac{1}{4}''$ diameter
$\times$ 1″ or $1\frac{1}{4}''$ long, unless ordered otherwise.
* Mounted on standard spindles $\frac{1}{4}''$ diameter $\times 1\frac{1}{4}''$ long.

Shape No.	Dia. Th.	Shape No.	Dia. Th.	Shape No.	Dia. Th.
W142	$\frac{3}{32} \times \frac{1}{4}$	W175	$\frac{3}{8} \times \frac{3}{8}$	W200	$\frac{3}{4} \times \frac{1}{8}$
W143	$\frac{1}{8} \times \frac{1}{8}$	W176	$\frac{3}{8} \times \frac{1}{2}$	W201	$\frac{3}{4} \times \frac{1}{4}$
W144	$\frac{1}{8} \times \frac{1}{4}$	W177	$\frac{3}{8} \times \frac{3}{4}$	W202	$\frac{3}{4} \times \frac{3}{8}$
W145	$\frac{1}{8} \times \frac{3}{8}$	W178	$\frac{3}{8} \times 1$	W203	$\frac{3}{4} \times \frac{1}{2}$
W146	$\frac{1}{8} \times \frac{1}{2}$	*W179	$\frac{3}{8} \times 1\frac{1}{4}$	W204	$\frac{3}{4} \times \frac{3}{4}$
W151	$\frac{7}{16} \times \frac{1}{8}$	W181	$\frac{1}{2} \times \frac{1}{16}$	*W205	$\frac{3}{4} \times 1$
W152	$\frac{7}{16} \times \frac{1}{4}$	W182	$\frac{1}{2} \times \frac{1}{8}$	*W208	$\frac{3}{4} \times 2$
W153	$\frac{7}{16} \times \frac{3}{8}$	W183	$\frac{1}{2} \times \frac{1}{4}$	*W209	$\frac{3}{4} \times 2\frac{1}{2}$
W154	$\frac{7}{16} \times \frac{1}{2}$	W184	$\frac{1}{2} \times \frac{3}{8}$	W211	$\frac{7}{8} \times \frac{1}{8}$
W157	$\frac{1}{4} \times \frac{1}{16}$	W185	$\frac{1}{2} \times \frac{1}{2}$	W212	$\frac{7}{8} \times \frac{1}{4}$
W158	$\frac{1}{4} \times \frac{1}{8}$	W186	$\frac{1}{2} \times \frac{3}{4}$	W215	$1 \times \frac{1}{8}$
W159	$\frac{1}{4} \times \frac{7}{16}$	W187	$\frac{1}{2} \times 1$	W216	$1 \times \frac{1}{4}$
W160	$\frac{1}{4} \times \frac{1}{4}$	*W188	$\frac{1}{2} \times 1\frac{1}{2}$	*W217	$1 \times \frac{3}{8}$
W162	$\frac{1}{4} \times \frac{3}{8}$	W191	$\frac{5}{8} \times \frac{1}{8}$	*W218	$1 \times \frac{1}{2}$
W163	$\frac{1}{4} \times \frac{1}{2}$	W192	$\frac{5}{8} \times \frac{1}{4}$	*W219	$1 \times \frac{3}{4}$
W164	$\frac{1}{4} \times \frac{3}{4}$	W193	$\frac{5}{8} \times \frac{3}{4}$	*W220	1×1
W167	$\frac{7}{16} \times \frac{1}{4}$	W194	$\frac{5}{8} \times \frac{1}{2}$	*W225	$1\frac{1}{4} \times \frac{1}{4}$
W170	$\frac{7}{16} \times \frac{1}{2}$	W195	$\frac{5}{8} \times \frac{3}{4}$	*W226	$1\frac{1}{4} \times \frac{3}{8}$
W173	$\frac{3}{8} \times \frac{1}{4}$	*W197	$\frac{5}{8} \times 2$	*W227	$1\frac{1}{4} \times \frac{1}{2}$
W174	$\frac{3}{8} \times \frac{1}{4}$	W199	$\frac{3}{4} \times \frac{1}{16}$		

Fig. 8.16   Table of Norton mounted Wheels and points.

that they should be machined from a high-tensile steel such as S.80 (EN 57) having an ultimate tensile strength in the order of 55 tons. Mild steel will not serve as there is the danger of the somewhat slender spindle bending and perhaps breaking under load. The small grinding wheels mentioned have, for the most part, a bore of $\frac{1}{4}''$ diameter and are obtainable in sizes from half to one inch with widths from a quarter to one inch.

Details of the special arbor made for these wheels are illustrated in *Fig. 8.17*.

The Arbor

The arbor takes the place of the collet chuck employed to hold the mounted points normally used. It is held in place by means of the collet closer and has a taper formed upon it of 30 degrees included angle to correspond with the female taper machined in the closer itself.

The $\frac{7}{32}''$ diameter shank of the arbor must be made a firm push

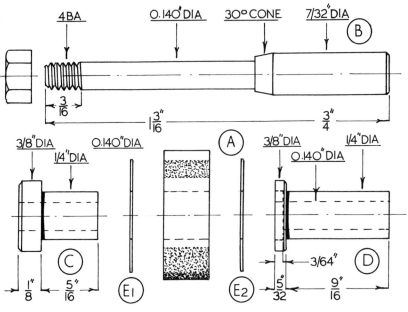

Fig. 8.17 Details of the small wheel arbor.

fit in the grinder spindle so as to eliminate all shake at this point; lapping both the arbor shank and the grinder spindle bore would ensure this. In doing so, however, make provision for the egress of trapped air or there may be difficulty in assembling the parts. A No. 60 drilled hole set radially at the internal end of the spindle bore would satisfy this requirement.

The various parts of the device need little critical mention with the exception of the two details E1 and E2. These are paper washers placed between the two mounting flanges C and D and the grinding wheel itself. The makers of grinding wheels will always supply these washers if requested; indeed, they are usually included when the wheels are supplied, for their use is essential in order to ensure that the wheels bed correctly and are held firmly when mounted on the arbor.

The $\frac{1}{4}''$ diameter of the spigot of the part C is made slightly longer than the nominal width of the wheel so that, when it is mounted, the grinding wheel and the washers can all be assembled together on the one part before thay are placed on the arbor. The face of the flange D is recessed to accommodate the distance the spigot of part C projects through the grinding wheel.

Alternative Arbor for Small Unmounted Grinding Wheels

For those who may prefer an arbor that can be inserted directly into the grinder collet the design illustrated in *Fig. 8.18* may be used. This arbor is intended for wheels $\frac{1}{4}''$ wide mounted close to the nose of the collet.

The seating for the arbor B is made long enough to accommodate the wheel and the two paper washers C1 and C2, leaving a small projection to register in the flange B1.

The making of the arbors is a single-operation exercise. In both types there is a long slender, or comparatively long and slender spindle to be machined; in one case 0.140″ diameter and in the other 0.125″ to engage the collet attached to the grinder spindle.

Deflection of these spindles during turning operations can be avoided if the lathe tailstock is brought up to support the work. It is sometimes difficult to make use of the normal centre fitted directly in to the tailstock itself, principally because there is little room in which to bring the centre to bear on the work. This difficulty can often be overcome if an extended lathe centre is mounted in the tailstock. Adequate support will then be given for the light cuts needed

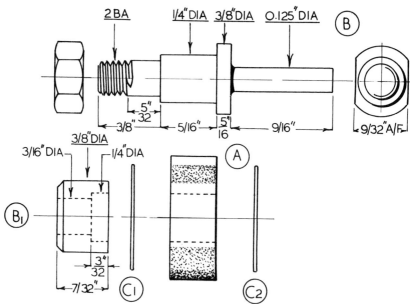

Fig. 8.18   Alternative arbor for direct insertion into the grinder collet.

to machine the work accurately. These extended centres can be made from silver steel, provided that the material is straight, and used with advantage in conjunction with the tailstock drill chuck. It is only necessary to chuck a short length of the steel, say a piece 3″ in length, and machine a 60 degree coned point on it having first set the material to run true in the 4-jaw independent chuck. The point is then polished, and finally hardened and tempered.

The following precautions should be taken when grinding operations are carried out in the lathe:—

(1) Do make sure that all lathe slides and working parts are adequately protected from abrasive dust.

(2) Do make sure, when truing grinding wheels, that the abrasive dust is discharged DOWNWARD and not up in the air.

(3) Do keep the grinding wheel keen by frequent truing. It is better to replace a worn wheel with a new one rather than to risk spoilt work by continuing to use worn out abrasives.

(4) DON'T attempt to remove an excess of material at a single pass of the grinding wheel. This would dull its cutting properties and lead to work out-of-parallel.

(5) Do make sure that the driving belt is correctly tensioned and is of a type designed specifically for the driving of grinding spindles.

Protecting the lathe may be achieved quite simply by spreading oily rags over the lathe bed and any other parts that may be subjected to abrasive dust. The oil allows the dust to adhere more easily to the rags which should, of course, be destroyed once the grinding operation is finished.

Protecting the rotating parts of the lathe is a more difficult matter. However, provided care is taken when the wheel is being trued, no special precautions are needed.

Driving Belts

The flat belts used for driving internal grinding spindles are of the endless pattern and are specially woven to ensure a smooth drive at all times.

The belts are made from cotton, sometimes impregnated with latex. This impregnation is a worthwhile provision since it greatly reduces any tendency to belt stretch, at the same time increasing the grip on the driving pulleys. When using a grinding spindle "from cold" it should be allowed to run idle for a while before taking a pass through the work. This will enable the driving belt to attain full flexibility and the spindle itself to reach maximum speed.

Fig. 8.19 A grinding set-up that is NOT recommended.

CHAPTER NINE

THE CUTTER GRINDER

IN THE LARGE PROFESSIONAL WORKSHOP the variety of milling cutters, end mills, reamers and saws that need to be sharpened, and sometimes modified to fit them for special duty, involves the use of equipment that is somewhat complex.

Basically the machines employed follow the lines of the cutter grinder illustration in *Fig. 9.1* and *Fig. 9.2*. These illustrations are taken from a catalogue printed in 1912 and they represent the type of simple machine then available. The grinder was driven from an overhead countershaft system with belting connected to the double-ended wheel head and the work head respectively. The table supporting the headstock of the workhead, and the tailstock used when long tools are being re-ground, is capable of swivelling when tapers have to be accommodated. It is traversed by hand and is provided with stops to limit the travel when necessary.

Both the Grinding Head, and the Workhead seen in *Fig. 9.1*, can be set at an angle to take care of particular re-sharpening problems. Some of these involve the use of the adjustable headstock and tailstock seen in the second illustration.

These basic requirements are embodied in all modern cutter grinders, which, of course, have self-contained driving motors that are now housed in the base of the machine, while the workhead is provided with its own driving motor.

A Cutter Grinding Attachment

The equipment just briefly described is, of course, primarily of interest in the professional workshop. The amateur worker, however, does not need such a complicated or expensive machine and can well do with a simple device that will enable him to re-sharpen any counterbores, end mills and spot-face cutters he may possess.

88

Fig. 9.1   The commercial cutter grinder 1912.

Fig. 9.2   The grinder set up for cutter servicing.

A Simple Cutter Grinding Attachment

Some 20 years ago, in Vol. II of their book "In the Workshop" the authors "Duplex" described a simple cutter grinding attachment that could be used with bench mounted grinding heads of the type commonly employed by amateurs for sharpening lathe tools. The matter was then dealt with very comprehensively, considerable time being devoted to describing the actual construction of the attachment. Now, however, space does not permit more than an abridgement of the original work leaving out constructional details. Those readers who need this information are advised to consult the public libraries where copies of the original work, now out of print, may be available. The type of end mill that the amateur makes for himself is depicted in *Fig. 9.3*, the pattern also applying to spot-face cutters sometimes called pin drills, and it is this form of cutter the attachment is designed to handle.

The general arrangement of the attachment when applied to the grinding machine is represented diagrammatically in *Fig. 9.4*.

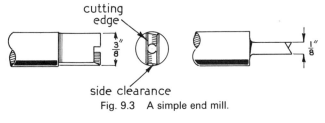

Fig. 9.3   A simple end mill.

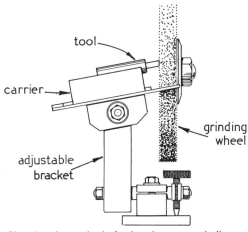

Fig. 9.4   Showing the method of using the cutter grinding attachment.

Reference to the subsequent drawings will show that the device consists essentially of two main components, the sliding carrier for holding and setting the cutter as shown in *Fig. 9.5*, and the adjustable bracket, *Fig. 9.6*, fitted with a tilting table on which the tool carrier slides to bring the point of the cutter into contact with the grinding wheel.

As will be seen, the carrier is guided by a fence and no V-slide is fitted; this is to enable the carrier to be readily removed for the purpose of resetting the cutter and, at the same time, to allow the table to be freed from any abrasive dust that may have collected during the grinding operation.

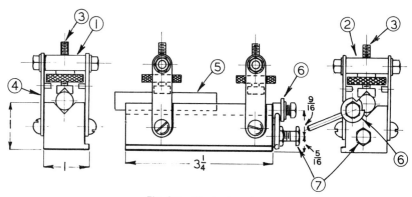

Fig. 9.5   The tool carrier.

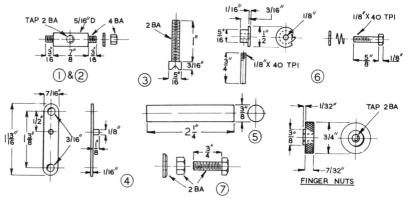

Fig. 9.6   Parts of the tool clamping device.

In the first instance the table was made in accordance with *Fig. 9.7*, but later, to give easier operation, a lever-feed mechanism was fitted; this will be described later.

An adjustable stop is fitted to the table to control the travel of the carrier when grinding either end-faces or the side surfaces of the cutter.

The vertical pillar carrying the table assembly pivots in the base bracket, and this movement, which is controlled by means of the adjusting-screw shown in the drawing, is used to set the feed when grinding the side faces of the cutter against the periphery of the wheel.

The Base Bracket

The complete table unit is held in a bracket attached to the bench top or to the base-board on which the grinding head is mounted.

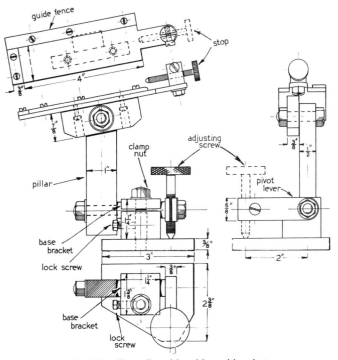

Fig. 9.7   The adjustable table and bracket.

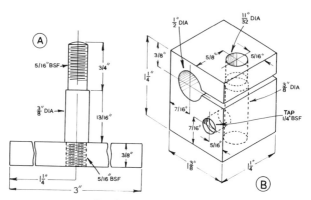

Fig. 9.8   The base bracket.

The construction of this bracket is similar to that supplied with the Potts drill grinding jig, so that the various attachments used with the grinding machine can be changed at will. In this way, either the drill grinding jig, the angular grinding rest, or the cutter grinder can quickly be mounted in place and correctly adjusted to the grinding wheel. Although the Potts bracket is machined from a casting this component can readily be built up from standard material. As shown in *Fig. 9.8* at A, the base piece is made from a length of $\frac{3}{8}''$ mild steel, which carries a shouldered and threaded stud screwed into place and lightly rivetted over at its lower end. The bracket itself is also made from mild steel to the dimensions given in *Fig. 9.8* at B.

The Lever Feed

As has been said earlier the tool carrier was originally designed to be moved along the table by hand in order to bring the cutter into contact with the grinding wheel. Although this method of operation gave good results, and many cutters were satisfactorily sharpened in this way, nevertheless at times it was found that the smooth travel of the carrier was hindered by abrasive grains that sometimes found their way to the surface of the table, particularly when the side faces of a cutter were being ground.

To overcome this difficulty, therefore, it was decided to fit a lever-feed to the tool carrier; this addition has greatly improved the working of the device under all conditions, and any obstruction caused by grinding dust now passed unnoticed.

The general appearance of the fitting is shown in *Fig. 9.9* whilst the dimensioned details are given in *Fig. 9.11.*

As will be seen, the bracket (1) carrying the lever (3) is attached to the table by three screws, and is tapped at its other end to receive the screw forming the pivot (2) for the lever. The ball-ended hand lever is frictionally controlled and carries one end of a ball-ended shaft (4) which connects it to the tool carrier.

The Connecting-Shaft

The method used to connect the hand lever to the tool carrier is depicted in *Fig. 9.12.* As will be observed a ball-ended rod (4) is used. This has a seating in the lever and is retained in place by means of two cycle links (5) these numbers referring to the detailed drawings in *Fig. 9.11.*

The ball at the other end of the rod engages a $\frac{1}{4}''$ hole drilled in the carrier, where it is retained in place by means of a latch. The details of the parts that comprise this fitment together with the position of the $\frac{1}{4}''$ diameter hole in the carrier are given in the illustration *Fig. 9.13.*

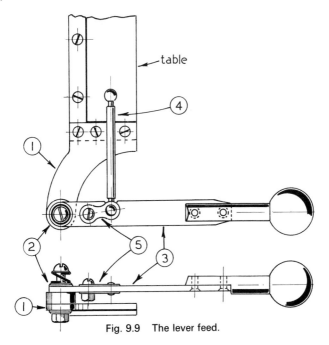

Fig. 9.9   The lever feed.

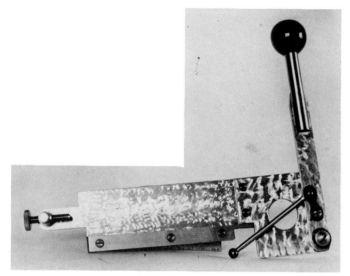

Fig. 9.10   The Lever feed.

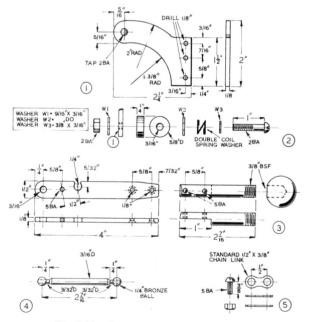

Fig. 9.11   Details of the feed-lever device.

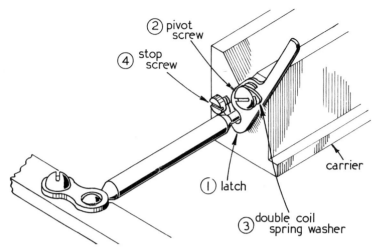

Fig. 9.12   Showing method of coupling the lever to the tool carrier.

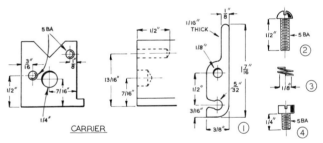

Fig. 9.13   Details of the latch.

Operating the Jig

A description of the process for sharpening an end-mill on both its end and side faces will illustrate the method of using the grinding jig. In the first place, to ensure that the end of the cutter is ground square, the clamp-nut and the lock-screw of the base bracket are slackened and the table is rotated to bring the guide fence into position at right angles to the surface of the grinding wheel, as represented diagrammatically in *Fig. 9.14*. The bracket lock-screw is then firmly tightened.

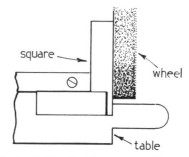

Fig. 9.14   Setting the table square with the wheel.

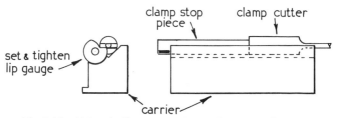

Fig. 9.15   Using the lip gauge and stop piece to set the cutter.

Next, as shown in *Fig. 9.15*, the cutter is mounted in the carrier with one cutting lip supported in a horizontal position on the lip gauge, and both the cutter clamp and the lip gauge pivot-screw are then tightened to ensure that the cutter is firmly located.

The cutter stop piece (5) in *Fig. 9.5*, is now brought into contact with the base of the cutter, and its clamp is tightened to ensure that, when the cutter is turned over to grind its other lip, it will be correctly end located. Slacken the bolt clamping the table bracket to the pillar, and, with the aid of a protractor or a suitable template, set the upper surface of the table to 10° in excess of a right angle as measured from the side of the wheel and as shown in *Fig. 9.16*; the table clamping bolt is then firmly locked.

Next place the tool carrier on the table in contact with the guide fence and, after slackening the base bracket clamp-bolt, rotate the pillar on its pivot to bring the centre line of the cutter into line with the wheel, as shown in *Fig. 9.17*; then tighten the base bracket clamp nut. The ball of the connecting rod attached to the hand lever can now be engaged with the tool carrier, and the latch is then closed.

The carrier is next moved to the right to bring the cutter into light contact with the grinding wheel, and the adjustable screw-stop is set to check any movement beyond this point.

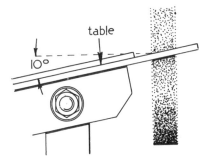

Fig. 9.16   Angular Setting of the table.

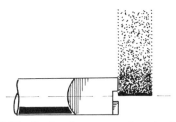

Fig. 9.17   Setting the cutter to the wheel.

When the carrier is traversed by means of the hand lever actuated by the left hand, the right hand is used to press the carrier downwards to maintain it in contact with the table, and at the same time pressure is also exerted to keep the carrier against the guide fence attached to the rear of the table.

The grinding machine is now started, and the tool carrier is traversed by means of the feed lever until its movement is arrested by the table stop. The stop is reset as required in order to allow the lip of the cutter to be lightly ground; the latch is then opened and the carrier is removed from the machine so that the other lip can be set against the lip gauge. For this purpose the tool clamp is slackened, but the setting of both the distance-piece and the lip gauge must remain unaltered.

The grinding operation is then continued in the same way on the second lip and the whole process is, if necessary, repeated until both lips are found to have a satisfactory finish.

This will complete the sharpening of the counterbore or a pin-drill. In the case of an end-mill, however, the side cutting edges will also need grinding from time to time.

For this purpose, the base bracket clamp-nut is slackened and the pillar is swung towards the operator in order to bring the cutter clear of the wheel. The cutter is then reset in the carrier until it projects sufficiently to allow the whole length of the side cutting edges to be brought into contact with the periphery of the wheel as the carrier is traversed on the table; when this adjustment has been made, the distance-piece is set and clamped in the new position.

As was previously pointed out, the centre line of the cutter should be approximately at the centre height of the wheel when the table is in the horizontal position, so that when the table is tilted to an angle of say, 10°, the cutter will make contact with the wheel well above the wheel centre. The effect of this is that the resulting contact will be over a small area only, and not along the whole length of the cutter's side cutting edges; this will ensure more accurate grinding and there will be less risk of overheating the tool.

Reference to *Fig. 9.18*, will show the position of the cutter in relation to the wheel when sharpening the side cutting edges and, at the same time, forming a cutting clearance behind these edges. For this purpose, the lip gauge is used to set the tool correctly to the wheel as judged by the eye, and a light trial cut will show if this has been done so that a cutting edge is produced in accordance with the original form.

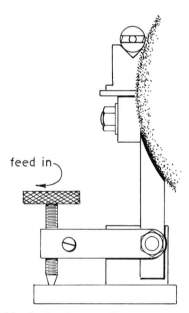

Fig. 9.18   Setting the cutter for grinding the side faces.

If the cutter is inserted in a hole in the drill gauge, the amount of clearance present can readily be estimated when the parts are viewed against the light.

When grinding the side faces, the travel of the tool carrier is adjusted by the table-stop as in the previous instance and, as re-presented in *Fig. 9.18*, the cutter is brought into contact with the wheel by turning the adjusting-screw fitted to the lever which is attached to the pivot shaft of the pillar.

After this adjustment has been made, the base bracket is clamped and a light cut is taken along the whole length of the edge; this is repeated on the other lip and the process is continued, with appropriate adjustments of the feed, until both lips are found to be correctly sharpened.

CHAPTER TEN

A MINIATURE
CUTTER GRINDER

THE CUTTER GRINDER to be described is the result of a process of evolution. Originally considered as a simple device for thinning the points of certain twist drills the machine has now been developed so that, in addition, it will deal with end-mills, slot drills, spot-face cutters and countersinks. It is also possible to re-point small drills with the device. The device itself is illustrated in *Figs. 10.1* and *10.2*.

The original conception of a device to thin drill points has proved

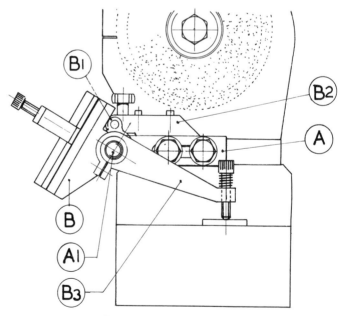

Fig. 10.1   The Cutter Grinder.

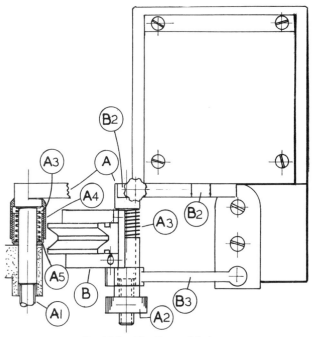

Fig. 10.2   The Cutter Grinder.

capable of extension to embrace most of the simple cutters employed in the small workshop. This development has involved the addition of two further cutter holders. These fit directly to the Rocking Platform Unit attached to the base of the Motor Mounting.

The principle upon which the grinder operates is that of rocking the work towards the periphery of the grinding wheel when thinning drills, and of passing the work across the face of the wheel when grinding spot-face cutters. The processes are illustrated in *Fig. 10.3* at A and B respectively.

The Motor and its Mounting

The Motor used with the Grinder is somewhat special. It is derived from a dynamo once fitted to a 1921 Rover 8 h.p. car, so the possibility of finding similar machines is remote; but this need not deter would be constructors who will be able to modify the designs themselves to incorporate one of the many types of motor available on

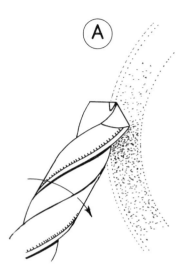
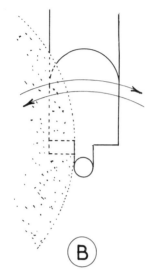

Fig. 10.3(A)   Thinning a drill point.   (B)   Sharpening a spot-face cutter.

the market. It should be mentioned, however that the machine should be capable of a speed of 5000 r.p.m., the correct speed for the grinding wheel fitted.

As an alternative a simple but robust grinding spindle could be made and used to replace the special motor illustrated.

The motor illustrated is a single-pole machine having its armature mounted eccentrically to the body. It runs at 5000 r.p.m. on 50 volts d.c. The Motor Mounting itself has been designed to allow the motor to be rotated or moved longitudinally and clamped in any desired position with reference to the work to be ground. This is an important provision as it materially increases the versatility of the machine. The Motor Mounting is seen in the illustration *Fig. 10.4.* The whole device is mounted on a hard wood block fitted with small rubber feet. These feet are in fact rubber tap washers obtainable from most ironmongers under the name "Holdtite".

The actual motor mounting was machined from a piece of light alloy. It is split along one side and is provided with a pair of clamp screws to secure the motor once it has been correctly set. In this connection it should be pointed out that, fortunately, the armature of the motor is offset in the motor carcase; consequently, it is possible to adjust the position of the grinding wheel in relation to the work

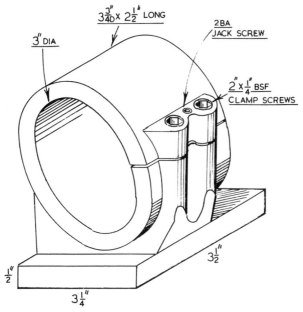

$3\frac{3}{40}$" x $2\frac{1}{2}$" LONG

3" DIA

2BA
JACK SCREW

2" x $\frac{1}{4}$" BSF
CLAMP SCREWS

$3\frac{1}{2}$"

$\frac{1}{2}$"

$3\frac{1}{4}$"

Fig. 10.4   The Motor Mounting.

by simply rotating the motor in its mounting and/or sliding it in or
out of the mounting in order to bring the wheel into contact with
the cutter to be ground. To this end a jack screw is fitted to the
mounting to ease the pressure after the clamp screws have been
released and so make it possible to move the motor freely.

The Rocking Platform Unit

The Rocking Platform unit is the basic element in the various cutter
holders. It consists of two main parts, the Bracket (A) and the
Platform (B). The Bracket is provided with a spindle (A), upon
which the platform is free to rock and an Adjusting Nut (A2)
controlling the longitudinal movement of the Platform and hence
the in-feed of the work. This movement is made against the Spring
(A3) encased in the Dust Covers (A4) and (A5) telescoping one
outside the other.

In order to retain uniformity of longitudinal feed and to avoid
working to a micrometer index a Limit Stop (B1), consisting of a

circular collar surrounding the Spring Dust Covers, is carried by a Bracket (B2) superimposed on the Bracket (A). The Bracket (B2) is provided with means for locking the Limit Stop in any desired position, whilst the Limit Stop, (B), has a pin engaging the Platform to prevent the latter from rocking too far away from the grinding wheel whilst cutters are either being adjusted or changed.

The principle upon which the grinder operates involves the use of an adjustable stop to control the rocking movement. The Stop (B3) in the form of a leg, is attached to a bar forming part of the Rocking Platform and may be rotated on the bar and then locked to provide a rough adjustment, whilst fine adjustment is effected by means of the spring loaded screw at the foot of the leg.

The Rocking Platform (B)

This part was made from a piece of hard light alloy as this material was to hand and apt for milling in the lathe, a process used for making most of the main parts of the device. An abutment shoulder is provided on the top surface to form a register for the V-block holding drills for point-thinning as well as the attachments for end-mill and spot-face cutter grinding. The V-blocks and the counter-sink attachment are held to the platform by clamps that engage slots formed in the blocks. A strip is attached to the upper surface opposite the abutment shoulder to serve as a guide when the V-block or the countersink attachment is being adjusted in relation to the platform.

The Bracket (A)

This part, made from mild steel, is provided with two slotted holes so that it may be moved in and out on the motor mounting platform to which it is attached by a pair of $\frac{1}{4}''$ BSF screws. It is bored at its outer end to receive the Spindle (A1).

The Spindle (A1)

This is machined from mild steel and is made a press-fit in the Bracket (A). Its outer end is threaded $\frac{5}{16}'' \times 26$ T.P.I. to accommodate the Adjusting Nut (A2). Note that, in order to provide some firmness in operation, the Adjusting Nut is fitted with a spring loaded brass pad bearing on the thread. The necessary adjustment of spring tension is effected by a grub screw set in the periphery of the nut.

We come now to the individual assemblies required for the different classes of cutter to be ground. The first of these is the equipment for thinning the point of a drill.

Drill Point Thinning

This equipment is simple. In addition to the basic rocking platform there is a V-block with clamp and register pin fitted to the platform and an index collar attached to the drill being treated. The complete assembly is seen in the illustration *Fig. 10.5.*

In connection with the index collars it should be noted that a collar is needed for each size of drill. From experience we have

Fig. 10.5   Assembly for drill point thinning.

found that for practical purposes a total of three sizes of drill with
their points thinned is sufficient. These are $\frac{1}{4}''$, $\frac{3}{8}''$ and $\frac{1}{2}''$ diameter
respectively.

Since the whole purpose of thinning the drill point is to enable the
drill to penetrate the work more rapidly and accurately, once a
pilot drill with its point thinned has been used the resulting hole can
be opened out with drills having normal points.

Equipment for Grinding End-Mills and Spot-Face Cutters

This consists of a further table provided with a peg that may be
clamped to the V-block mounted on the Rocking Platform, and a
mounting for the index finger.

In addition there is an adjustable stop attached to the table
enabling cutters mounted in a second V-block to be retained in their
correct location during grinding operations. These details may be
seen in the illustration *Fig. 10.6*. In order to provide clearance when
grinding spot-face cutters and the like, the table is tilted at the correct
angle as illustrated in *Fig. 10.7* and clamped by its peg in the V-block;
while the index finger is set to engage one tooth of the cutter being
ground.

Fig. 10.6   Set-up for grinding end-mills.

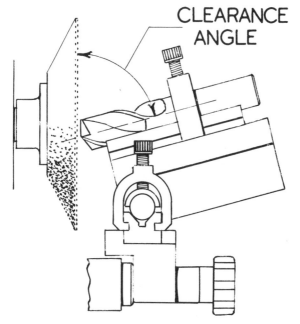

Fig. 10.7   Obtaining the clearance angle.

Equipment for Grinding Angular Cutters

An example of the type of angular cutter requiring attention from time-to-time is the countersink. For the most part these have four cutting teeth though there are some with ten or more cutting edges and these are really not worth the trouble of a regrind. The grinder being described, however, has been found to deal with them quite adequately but the 4-lipped countersink is a more serviceable tool and, being somewhat more expensive, deserves proper care.

In order to ensure that, during the grinding process, each cutting lip is adequately indexed, a special holder has been devised with an index plate engaging a pin fitted to the V-block. The plate has four slots to engage the pin enabling either 2-lipped or 4-lipped cutters to be sharpened. The set up is illustrated in *Fig. 10.8* where the cutter holder can also be seen. This part is illustrated by itself in *Fig. 10.9.*

The basis of the arrangement is a mounting for the V-block enabling it to be set and locked at any angle that may be required in sharpening cutters such as countersinks. For the most part counter-sinks have an included angle of either 60° or 90° as these angles are

Fig. 10.8   Grinding a countersink.

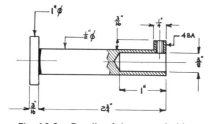

Fig. 10.9   Details of the cutter holder.

easily set by applying a protractor to the V-block on its mounting.
 The mounting is clamped to the working platform and may be
adjusted on the platform to accommodate the cutter being ground.

Grinding Angular Cutters

A combination of the attachments for grinding countersinks and end-mills enables angular cutters with more than four teeth to be ground. The end-mill attachment is provided with an indexing finger and this is also used to index the teeth of multi-tooth countersinks for example. Indexing, is, of course, achieved by registering the index finger with each tooth of the cutter in turn.

The arrangement is shown in *Fig. 10.10* whilst the details of the mounting for the index finger are given in *Fig. 10.11*.

Grinding Piloted Countersinks

There may be readers who, in company with the author, need to sharpen countersinks that are provided with pilots. The miniature cutter grinder will deal with them as may be seen in the illustration *Fig. 10.12*. The countersink is again mounted in the cutter holder so that it can be accurately indexed and is set in a V-block angled to suit the countersink being ground. The V-block itself rides on a packing block to which it may be locked at any angle required.

Relief behind the cutting edges is obtained by slightly offsetting

Fig. 10.10   Set-up to show the index finger in use.

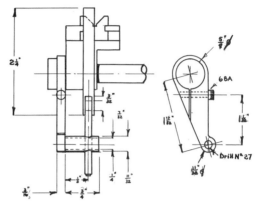

Fig. 10.11   Details of the mounting for the index finger.

Fig. 10.12   Set-up for grinding piloted countersinks.

the countersink so that the surface of the grinding wheel impinges *behind* the cutting edges in the first place.

Using the Grinder

Before the grinder is used the wheel itself must be dressed to ensure that its surface is in good order. Of course the most convenient way to do this is to employ a properly mounted industrial diamond clamped in the appropriate V-block and pass this across the face of the wheel in the same way as a cutter being ground. But a mounted diamond is an expensive article and equally good results can be obtained by holding a piece of coarse carborundum against the wheel.

Once the wheel is dressed, and it should be emphasised that regular dressing is required to prevent glazing of the work when the wheel has become dulled, grinding can commence.

Attachment for Grinding Circular Saws

If they are to do their work efficiently the small circular saws used in the workshop for slitting operations, for slotting screw heads and work of a similar nature need re-sharpening from time-to-time.

In the small workshop these saws will in all probability vary very much in size and will, doubtless, also have a wide range of bore diameters. In the author's workshop these saws have bores varying from $\frac{1}{2}''$ dia. to $1\frac{1}{8}''$ so the attachment illustrated in *Fig. 10.13* has been designed to accommodate a wide range of measurements in this respect. It will accept saws from $1\frac{3}{4}''$ to $3''$ diameter, having bore diameters from $\frac{1}{2}''-1\frac{1}{8}''$.

The attachment is secured to the lower of the two V-blocks used for cutter mounting by means of the stud (2) seen in the illustration *Fig. 10.14*. This stud, having a hub $\frac{1}{2}''$ diameter, secures the mounting plate (1) to the V-block, and is provided with shouldered washers to accommodate the different cutter bore sizes that need to be catered for. As will be appreciated the saw to be sharpened is gripped between the mounting plate and the shoulder washer, pressure being applied through the washer (3) by the finger nut (4).

In the process of sharpening, the saws need to be indexed tooth-by-tooth. This is effected by the index finger used for operations previously mentioned. This finger with its accompanying mount is attached to the bars (5) fastened to the underside of the mounting plate (1).

Fig. 10.13   Set-up for sharpening small circular saws.

Wheels for Saw Sharpening

When sharpening saws the grit size of the wheel needs to be chosen
with some care. Saws with coarse pitch teeth can be ground most
effectively with wheels having a grit size from 60–80. But the smaller
saws with close-pitch teeth need wheels with much finer grit, say up
to 120 or over. The reason for this is the fact that, in the latter case,
unless the grit is fine, it will be impossible to impart a sharp corner
to the wheel and this is essential when finishing a saw with close-
pitch teeth.

   As has been said, wheels are trued most effectively with an
industrial diamond; but a piece of really coarse carborundum will
also perform the same service. In fact some professional cutter
grinders prefer the carborundum, maintaining that it leaves the

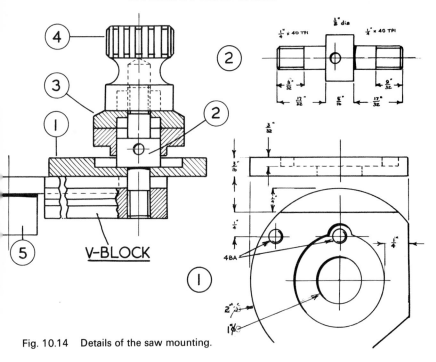

Fig. 10.14   Details of the saw mounting.

wheel in a more open and therefore a better cutting condition, a view with which the author has some sympathy.

It is important to set the saw accurately in relation to the grinding wheel. If this is not done the crests of the teeth will be out of square and may be as shown in *Fig. 10.15* at A and not as they should be as depicted in *Fig. 10.15* at B.

To this end the surface of the saw mounting platform must be aligned with the axis of the grinding wheel as seen in the diagram *Fig. 10.16*.

Packing or shim equal in thickness to half the width of the saw itself is interposed between the straight edge and the surface of the mounting platform. In this way the tops of the teeth will be ground at right angles to the sides of the saw.

Set-up for Grinding Circular Saws

Circular wood saws up to 5 inches diameter may be re-sharpened on the cutter grinder. The procedure involves two separate opera-

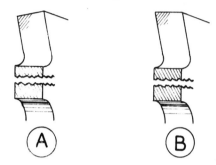

Fig. 10.15   Showing the effect of incorrect saw mounting.

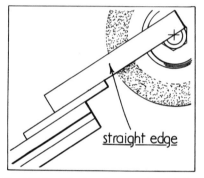

Fig. 10.16   Aligning the mounting platform.

tions. The first to grind the front face of each tooth, whilst the second allows the "backing-off" of the teeth to be maintained. These two operations are depicted diagrammatically in the illustration *Fig. 10.17* at A and B respectively.

In order to grind the tooth faces at (A) the saw is mounted at an angle to the centre line of the grinding spindle while the grinding wheel is mounted with its vertical face towards the driving motor.

The position of the wheel and saw tooth is shown in the illustration *Fig. 10.18.*

This arrangement allows the wheel to be passed across the face of each tooth, the indexing of the teeth being controlled by the finger stop previously described whilst the in-feed of the wheel is checked by the stop (A4) in *Fig. 10.2.*

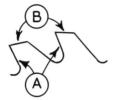

Fig. 10.17   Grinding circular wood saws.

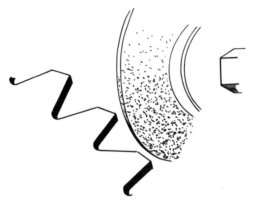

Fig. 10.18   Relation of saw tooth and grinding wheel when gulleting.

Grinding the Back-off

The Backing-off of the saw teeth is achieved by rocking the saw backwards and forwards across the face of the cup-wheel, now turned with its working surface away from the driving motor. The set-up is depicted in the illustration *Fig. 10.19*. The teeth are indexed by the finger previously mentioned and the depth of the grinding is controlled by the stop described earlier.

The saws supplied for use with electric drills marketed by Black & Decker and others are of a type suitable for both ripping and cross cutting. After re-sharpening several times the teeth of the saw will need setting. This is an operation described in detail in the book "Sharpening Small Tools", published by Model & Allied Publications Ltd. Whilst the description of the operation applies the more particularly to hand saws, the method or principles used for setting circular saws is similar.

The Grinding Machine

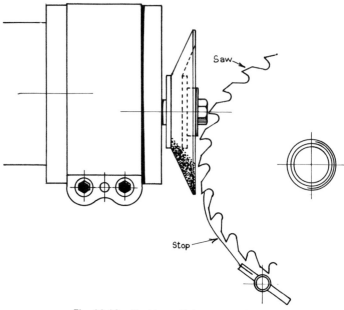

Fig. 10.19   Backing-off the saw teeth.

CHAPTER ELEVEN

THE FLEXIBLE SHAFT GRINDER

THE USE OF A POWER-DRIVEN TOOL that can be held in the hand and applied to the work for drilling, grinding or polishing purposes has long been recognised as a convenient method of carrying out this type of operation, the more particularly when the work itself cannot be carried to the tool.

A typical example that may well have been the forerunner of all flexible shaft machines is the dental drill of evil memory. From the operator's point of view such equipment has all the sensitivity the dentist demands; a fact that, many years ago, may well have impressed itself on some unwilling but observant patient in the dentist's chair. Be that as it may, flexible shaft grinders began to be produced for use in industry until, over the years, a wide range of machines has become available.

The small workshop and the amateur have not been forgotten, so they may obtain small equipment most suited to their needs. Typical examples are marketed by B. O. Morris Limited of Coventry, under the trade name "Morrisflex". Their "Modelmaker" Machine, illustrated in *Fig. 11.1*, is described as having been produced to meet the requirements of Toolroom operatives, Dental Laboratories and model workshops. The "Modelmaker" equipment is designed to be hung from the workshop ceiling in the manner depicted by *Fig. 11.2* where two of the machines are seen in operation.

The handpiece is provided with a range of interchangeable collets that enable the user to employ a wide variety of burrs, mounted points, abrasive discs and the like, all being obtainable from the manufacturers.

The advent of equipment suitable for use by the Do-it-Yourself fraternity has led to the production of a Morrisflex shaft that may be attached to any of the electric hand drills now on the market. The Morrisflex Flexshaft Kit 753, illustrated in *Fig. 11.3*, consists of a 40 inch long flexible shaft having a $\frac{1}{4}''$ diameter flexible core.

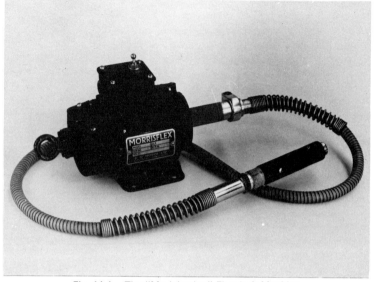

Fig. 11.1   The "Modelmaker" Flexshaft Machine.

The core is provided with a $\frac{1}{4}''$ diameter spindle for engagement in the chuck of the hand drill or in the bench drill if more convenient.

The handpiece at the opposite end of the flexshaft has a $\frac{3}{8}''$ diameter spindle threaded 24 T.P.I. and fitted with $\frac{1}{4}''$ Keyless chuck which may be used to mount twist drills, rotary burrs and all the other tools that are available with shanks.

The drill chuck can be removed and the two nuts and washers that are provided can be substituted to hold small grinding wheels, wire wheels and polishing mops having a $\frac{3}{8}''$ diameter bore.

The flexshaft runs in phosphor bronze bearings at both ends of the casing and the makers recommend that it should be maintained at a fairly high speed, for example as near to 3000 r.p.m. as possible. It should not, however, be run at the lower speeds available in some makes of electric drill, nor should it be used with the low-speed attachments sometimes supplied.

Low-voltage Equipment

Readers who have delved into other books by the author will remember that he has some leanings towards equipment powered with low-voltage electric motors.

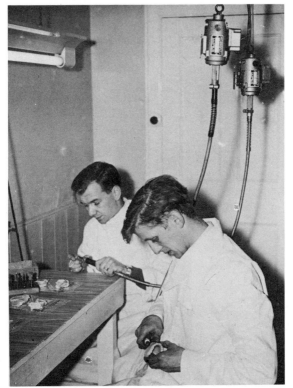

Fig. 11.2 "Modelmaker" Flexshaft Machines in use.

The device to be described represents another of the tools in the author's shop for which the power is supplied by a low-voltage motor. The motor itself, running for the most part at 12 volts d.c. but normally rated for 27 volts d.c., is one originally forming part of the fuel system of a high-performance aeroplane. It is an extremely powerful shunt-wound machine easily capable of ar y work that light flexible shaft equipment might be expected to encounter. The motor unit itself is illustrated in *Fig. 11.4*. This consists of a mounting enabling the motor to be slung overhead and a coupling device for the flexible shaft itself. The details of the mounting are given in *Fig. 11.5*. The motor itself is seated in a register on a ring 'C' and is held in place by a clamp ring 'D'. The coupling device is made up from a cover plate 'A', also registering with the ring 'C', and a sleeve 'B' covering the connector 'E' that engages the squared end of the flexible shaft itself.

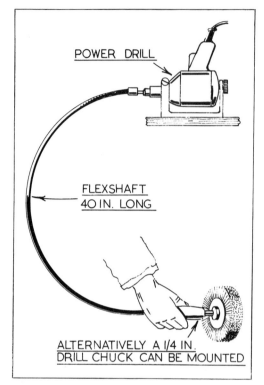

POWER DRILL

FLEXSHAFT
40 IN. LONG

ALTERNATIVELY A 1/4 IN.
DRILL CHUCK CAN BE MOUNTED

Fig. 11.3   The Morrisflex flexshaft Kit No. 753.

A dust cover for the motor, made from a discarded fruit can, is held down to the motor mounting ring by a triangular plate from which the unit is suspended by three rods seen in the illustration.

The Flexible Shaft

The connection between the motor and the handpiece that holds the various tools or grinding wheels is a flexible shaft of the type used for driving speedometers or revolution counters. Many of these components were made for aircraft purposes at one time or another, and it is a pair of these shafts that are used by the author. The one normally employed is three feet long whilst the other, brought into play when especially required, is some seven feet in length, they were obtained on the surplus market where doubtless similar flexible shafts are still available.

Fig. 11.4   The low-voltage motor unit.

The Handpiece

The illustration *Fig. 11.6* depicts the handpiece with a rotary file in place. The assembly of the parts comprising the handpiece is to be seen in the sectional drawing *Fig. 11.7*. The handpiece consists of a fluted body (A) housing a ball-bearing assembly comprising a pair of deep-groove ball races at the outer end of the component and a single race at the driving end. The races are held in place by a pair of end caps (A1) and (A2). The races support the spindle (B) over which a tubular distance piece (B2) is slipped to secure the inner components of the ball races; the necessary pressure is applied by the threaded connector (B1) which is engaged by the squared end of the inner cable.

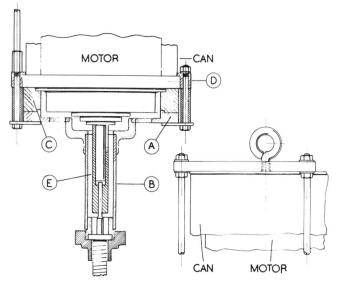

Fig. 11.5   The Motor Mounting.

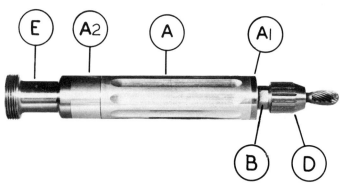

Fig. 11.6   The Handpiece.

The outer cable casing is secured to an extension (E) screwed into the end cap (A2) and is held in place by a narrow hexagon but forming a part of the complete flexible shaft assembly. The spindle (B) is seen in the illustration *Fig. 11.8*. Here the ball races are shown in place together with the end cap (A1) but not the sleeve (B2). The spindle itself is threaded at its inner end to accept the connector (B1) and the opposite end is chambered and threaded to accept the collet

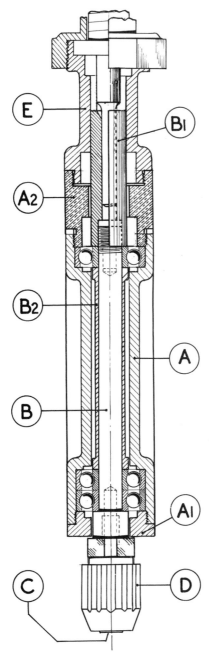

Fig. 11.7   The Handpiece in section.

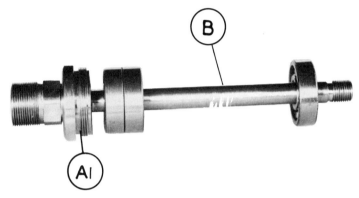

Fig. 11.8   The Spindle and bearings.

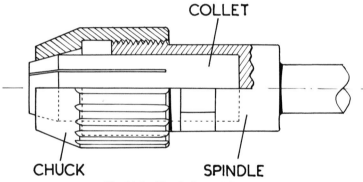

Fig. 11.9   The Collet and Chuck.

(C) and chuck (D) seen in the illustration *Fig. 11.9.* Both spindle and chuck, which is really a collet closer having an internal taper, are threaded $\frac{1}{2}'' \times 40$ t.p.i. The fine thread allows the user to tighten the chuck with the fingers only, the spindle having a square machined on it so that a spanner can be used to hold the spindle stationary whilst the chuck is being rotated.

The collet is parallel, and is split three ways by the machining operation depicted in *Fig. 11.10.* Using the lathe milling attachment for the purpose illustrated, all the machining needed to produce the collet can be carried out at one setting so that the component is complete when parted off from the parent material.

Fig. 11.10   Slitting the Collet.

Tools for use in the Handpiece

The handpiece may be used to hold a variety of tools, some of these being illustrated in *Fig. 11.11*. They comprise rotary files, wire brushes and mounted points; small grinding wheels fitted with integral spindles by means of which the points may be gripped in the handpiece. The spindles used for the points, and also for rotary files, are made to three standard sizes, the larger being 6 mm. and $\frac{1}{4}''$ diameter while the smaller shanks are made $\frac{1}{8}''$ diameter.

Fig. 11.11   Tools for use with the handpiece.

Rotary Files

Whilst not precisely abrasive tools, the Rotary Files or Burrs may be used with flexible shaft machines (or indeed, as the makers claim, directly with an electric hand drill) and deserve a few words of comment.

(1) Their shanks should be inserted well down into the chuck or handpiece where they should be firmly gripped.

(2) Should the teeth tend to clog, as may well happen when filing aluminium, the trouble can be averted or at least alleviated, by rubbing the teeth with a piece of candle or a grease pencil whichever is available.

(3) When using rotary files they should be traversed across the work from right to left for the fast removal of stock, and from left to right for fine finishing the work. The procedure is depicted diagrammatically in *Fig. 11.12.*

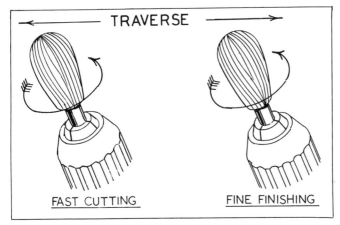

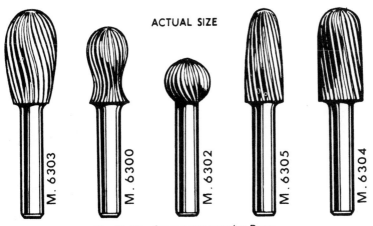

Fig. 11.12   Using the Rotary File.

(4) Rotary Files should be applied with a firm even pressure taking care that they do not chatter or bounce on the work.

The Burrs are obtainable in many sizes and shapes, a representative selection being illustrated FULL SIZE in *Fig. 11.13.*

The particular selection depicted is made especially by Morrisflex for use in electric drills and in the Flexible Shaft Attachment described earlier. The shanks of these Burrs are $\frac{1}{4}''$ diameter.

ACTUAL SIZE

M.6303   M.6300   M.6302   M.6305   M.6304

Fig. 11.13   Some representative Burrs.

CHAPTER TWELVE

GRINDING ATTACHMENT FOR THE ENGRAVER

THE ATTACHMENT NOW TO BE DESCRIBED formed part of the equipment for the engraving machine featured in "Model Engineer" by Duplex some years ago. It is a very simple device that gave perfect results; so it was thought proper to bring the attachment to the notice of readers who may not have seen the original articles and could, perhaps, apply the principles in other contexts.

The attachment itself is illustrated in *Fig. 12.1*, depicting the device in place on the Duplex engraving machine, which some may remember was based on the column, stand and work table of the drilling machine available from E. W. Cowell of Watford.

As will be seen the cutter holder itself is attached to the column of the engraver while the grinding wheel employed is mounted in the chuck forming part of the engraving machine spindle.

Principles of Operation

The method by which the cutter is ground may be understood from the diagram *Fig. 12.2*. Cutters used in an engraving machine are similar in form to the D-bit having a single cutting edge as depicted in the left of the illustration. It is only necessary, therefore, to provide relief behind this edge, a requirement easily met with the swash plate system depicted. The swash plate itself is mounted on a sleeve surrounding the cutter holder and, as may be inferred, is adjustable so that it is, in effect, a variable lift face cam. Relief is obtained behind the cutting edge when the cutter holder is rotated with the cam in contact with the micrometer stop. The cutting edge itself has first to be set to make contact with the grinding wheel when the cam is at its most elevated position, then when the cutter holder is rotated against the stop, the cutter is allowed to slide forward thus imparting the necessary relief.

128

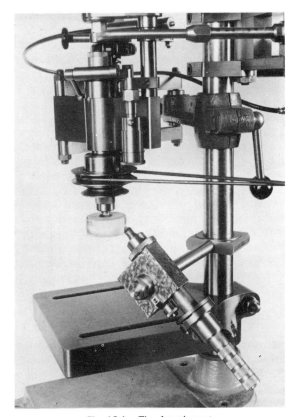

Fig. 12.1   The Attachment.

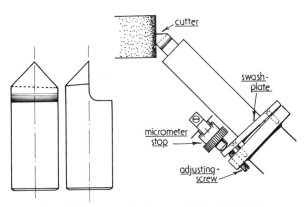

Fig. 12.2   Schematic diagram of the attachment.

The stop itself is engraved in $\frac{1}{1000}''$ enabling the operator to control the depth of cut, while the swash plate is elevated by an adjusting screw against which it is secured by three countersink screws.

The cutter is held in the collet set in the top of the holder and is secured by a closer knurled so that it can be finger operated.

The Mounting Bracket (A)

This component has an important part to play in the working of the attachment for apart from supporting the device as a whole, it controls the angle that is imparted to the point of the cutter.

The details of the bracket are given in *Fig. 12.3*. It comprises a clamp, by means of which it is secured to the machine column, and a horizontal shouldered member to accommodate the body of the attachment. The horizontal member projects through the body and is furnished with a nut and large-diameter washer enabling the user to clamp the block against the shoulder at any angle he may desire.

The Cutter Holding Assembly (Fig. 12.4)

This assembly comprises the Body (B) on which is mounted a raised platform (D) for the engraving of the zero line used when reading the micrometer stop (C).

As has been mentioned earlier the cutter itself is secured in its collet by the ring nut or chuck (G) that is mounted on the cutter holder (F). The sleeve (H), carrying the swash plate (K) is secured by the knurled screw seen projecting from the sleeve. All these components are detailed in the illustration *Fig. 12.5*. In addition this illustration also depicts the friction devices that are fitted to the micrometer stop (C) and the sleeve (H) respectively. That for the micrometer stop is depicted at (E) while the friction device for the knurled screw will be seen to form part of that component itself.

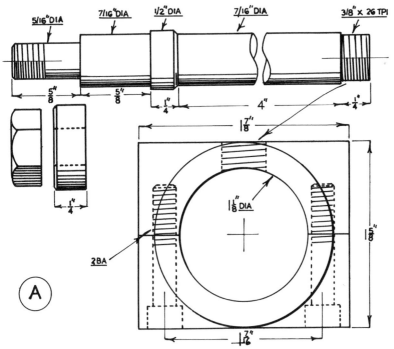

Fig. 12.3   The mounting bracket.

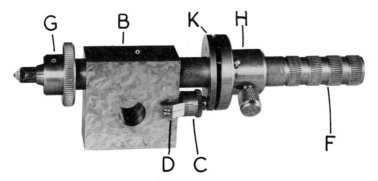

Fig. 12.4   The Body and Cutter Holder.

132

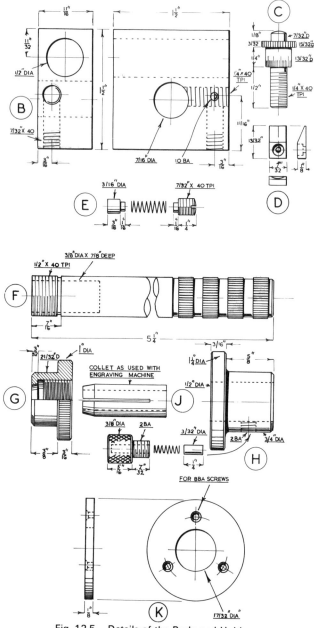

Fig. 12.5   Details of the Body and Holder.

INDEX

Index

Index

Norton mounted points, 80

Operating the cutter grinding jig, 95–99
Oxide, aluminium, 3

Paper washers, 8
Parting tool, 28
Phillipp, 8
Plane iron, 3
Plate, base, 65–66
Plate, swash, 128, 130
Point, drill, 41, 42
Points, mounted, 67, 75, 80, 125
Polishing, 6
Potts jig, 37, 48, 92
Precautions when grinding, 85

Rake, side, 28, 30
Rake, top, 27
Relieved flanges, 8, 9
Rest, angular grinding, 27–40, 92
Rotary files, 125–127
Royen, L. van, 45

Saddle, 63
Sandstone, 2, 3
Saw sharpening, wheels for, 112–113
Shaft, flexible, 117–120
Sharpening, 6
Sharpening, end-mill, an, 95–99
Side clearance, 28
Side rake, 28
Simple angular rest, 31–33
Simple tool grinder, 11–19
Slot drills, 100
Spindle, grinding, 17, 59, 62, 67, 68, 124
Spindle, mounting, 75
Spot-face cutters, 100, 104, 106
Stone, Arkansas, 1
Stone, Washita, 1

Stop, limit, 103, 104
Striking gear, 12
Supply, electrical, 24
Surface grinding, 9
Swash plate, 128, 130

Test indicator, 63–65
Thinning the drill point, 42–45, 104–106
Tool carrier, 90, 92, 93, 96, 98, 99
Tool grinder, simple, 11–19
Tool, knife, 28
Tool, parting, 28
Toolpost, 67
Toolpost grinder, 67–69
Tools for use with the handpiece, 125–127
Toolpost grinder, lubricating the, 79
Toolpost grinder, using the, 79–85
Transformer, 70
Truing the grinding wheel, 78, 79
Tungsten Carbide, 27
Twist drill jig, 45–53

Universal Grinding Wheel Co., 50
Using the toolpost grinder, 79–85

V-belting, 13
V-block, 104, 106, 107
Vinci, Leonardo da, 6

Washers, "Holdtite", 102
Washers, paper, 83
Washita Stone, 1
Wheel dressing, 111, 112
Wheel, grinding on side of, 15–17
Wheels, cup, 50
Wheels, grinding, 6, 17, 50, 51
Wheels, saw sharpening, for, 112–113
Wire brushes, 125
Wolf grinders, 24–26, 30

135